MOM

KILLS

KIDS

AND

SELF

A NOVEL

by Alan Saperstein

MACMILLAN PUBLISHING CO., INC.

New York

MOM
KILLS
KIDS
AND
SELF.

Macmillan Publishing Co., Inc.
866 Third Avenue, New York, N.Y. 10022
Collier Macmillan Canada, Ltd.

LIBRARY OF CONGRESS CATALOGING IN PUBLICATION DATA

Saperstein, Alan.
Mom kills kids and self.

I. Title.
PZ4.S2416Mo [PS3569.A58]   813'.5'4   79-12039
ISBN 0-02-606880-X

First Printing 1979

Designed by Jack Meserole

Printed in the United States of America

For Lynn

Friday

When I arrived home from work I found my wife had killed our two sons and taken her own life. The cat was only sleeping.

From the back doorway I could see their awkward bodies reflected in the mirrored wall opposite them. Stupidly I walked to the mirror, came up against it, my eyes fixed on their reflections. I touched my hand to the image of my wife's stillness. My own face was a blur. But I could change focus and stare at the sharp face staring back. Of the two tableaux, mine was the sadder.

"Wake up, get up, stop it," I said, wondering whether to go so far as to shake them.

The cat stirred. She stretched and tiptoed around the tiny balls of shit and the empty glass of iced coffee on the dining room carpet.

Of course I knew that's what did it—the little one's messy refusal to be toilet trained and the seven-year-old's constant sneaking down of his mother's habitual iced coffee. My mind reenacted her discovering the trail of shitballs and becoming furious and then, in the middle of cleaning up after the little one, noticing that the older one had once again stolen her iced coffee while she had gone for the Wipe 'n Dipes, and I could picture the veins in her slender neck redden and bulge as she screamed her unheeded reprimands, and I could hear her hoarse screams turn into sarcasm and then despair and then loathing and then murder.

I turned off the chili, which was black in the pot.

I picked up the tiny balls of shit with a paper towel and took them outside to the ashcan so there wouldn't be a smell in the house.

I put the glass right, for it was on its side, the traces of coffee still in it having turned to film.

Still there was no shock, only a familiar terror.

There were nights, one in particular, when I'd sat on the window seat in the living room, wondering where the three of them were past the children's bedtime. I would look out onto the street and try to tell our car by the headlamps two blocks away as they projected less and less of the curve of our road. But I never knew our car that well. Not from the outside.

As each car drove closer, my heart paused until I could see it was not ours, and I was filled again with a thumping sense of dread. It wasn't a feeling that something terrible was about to happen, but that it had happened already and I was about to find it out. Then would come sorrow, a trickling pity that I had been reading or watching TV or grabbing a sandwich at the precise moment their car burst into flames or the enormous rapist tore their twelve limbs apart or impenetrable traffic kept an ambulance from arriving in time to contain my little boy's ruptured appendix.

There was terror in the telephone ever poised to spring its awful sound at me, terror at the back door, under the front door, on every scrap of paper, a black terror hidden within the mailbox out on the lawn, terror everywhere and every way bad news could take me by surprise.

But the house remained quiet.

•

When I arrived home from work I found my wife had killed our two sons and taken her own life.

My one way of dealing with death was impractical. A joke could make it all disappear. But my wife could not laugh. My wife could not compound the joke and make me laugh.

Suddenly all I could see were spots of dirt on my glasses.

She may have left a joke behind. That would be like her. I began to search the house from where I stood.

Our cat used to like staring into a Corot landscape when it hung above the television set, and my wife once thought to draw the cat upon the glass. Months went by before I noticed, but my wife never hinted. Patience would be even easier for her now.

But no, these murders would not have been premeditated. The idea may have been growing inside her for some time, the wild courage to commit murder may have come to a slow boil, but the act itself had to have been unrehearsed.

From the looks of them, she would have begun by beating the older boy, slapping and punching him in the face over and over again, grabbing his head and pounding it into the edge of the dining room table; then, confused and driven even madder by a new screaming, she would have smothered the little one's sobbing panic. Suddenly there would be quiet, and an instant of the peace she had once known—only an instant—before the unburdening of her misery became a new misery too terrible to consider. She would run to the bathroom, fling aside bottles and tubes in pursuit of a blade, run back to her children, slash crazily at her wrists, sit down beside them, take them into her blood-streaked arms, and then run, run, run to meet her death. She would have had no chance to draw herself hanging from the limb of one of Corot's trees.

.

When I arrived home from work I found my wife had killed our two sons and taken her own life.

I uncovered a blast of foul, black steam from the pot on the stove and said, "Hi, hon, what's for dinner?" But she did not laugh. She did not bounce to her feet and pirouette into the kitchen to greet me. My little one didn't race into my legs and ask what I brought him. The seven-year-old didn't automatically beg me to play a game knowing my answer would be a tired, "Maybe later."

Instead there were strangers in my house as if I had pulled into the wrong driveway and let myself in through someone else's back door. Whose wife was this, whose children?

I tried to remember what their voices sounded like, but I couldn't, and I worried that maybe I had never listened intently enough. But then I tried to remember my own voice, and all I could hear in my mind was a faraway distortion, a telephone voice, a TV moderator babbling in another room. I was a stranger myself.

It struck me that I needed to inspect the house from top to bottom. Perhaps I was looking for a catastrophe, an overflowing toilet bowl, a busted boiler, a leaky roof, some real evidence of the feeling I had that my life was caving in.

The cat followed me throughout the house, sneaking underfoot as I climbed the stairs, squealing once when I stepped on her paw. In the little one's room she stalked a feather that had worked its way out of a pillow. She was having a fit of energy as extreme as one of her catnaps in which only a good poke or a sharp noise could rouse her before she was ready. This was her life—deep, restorative sleep alternating with a hyperactive entertainment never meant to accomplish anything more than induce sleep again. And yet she had the healthy look and temperament which were the pride and purpose of her continuing breed. Hers was such a simple life that I felt I knew her intimately and completely. When we were alone in a room, both of us drowsy in front of the television, for example, I'd hug her to my face and whisper that I knew how she felt and that I knew she knew how I felt, too. But, of course, her true kinship was with my wife. The two seemed to be able to read each other's minds. Only her key in the latch would wake the cat from one of her curled, heaving, comatose naps. Only her kissnoise persuaded the cat to come for food. And when the cat meowed in any of her various inflections, my wife understood. One meant hunger, one meant brush me, one meant cold, hot, outside (only as far as the screened breezeway), another meant up into the dish pantry, or down into the broom closet, or chase me, let me stalk you and then quick as a rat you turn on me and try to catch me.

If she were more mine than my wife's, I'd have let her outside. Beyond the breezeway. But my wife did not want her outside. It was okay to let the cat breathe this other life through the breezeway screens, okay for the outdoors to blow its cool movement through her fur, against her eyes, into her complex ears; but no, she could not join its movement, could not capture any part of it with claws or teeth. I always said I agreed with my wife that the cat didn't really want to go beyond the breezeway. And watching her now as she pounced on the little feather with claws and teeth, sped off, snuck up, pounced again, I thought, maybe my wife is right. Was right.

He had good little fingers, I thought, scanning the little one's room. Beads he had strung lay on the rich green carpeting. A family of miniature animals and people were tucked into one of my wife's open-toed slippers. They snuggled as peacefully and naturally as if they were in a children's story. Several cars and trucks of dramatically different sizes were parked neatly along the baseboard molding. Even where toys were not in their proper places, they were nevertheless in special places: a stuffed gorilla in a play shopping cart, a hobbyhorse stuck through a dresser drawer pull, equal piles of marbles in each compartment of an egg carton.

The older boy treasured little, by comparison. His room across the hall was schizophrenia-swept: torn pages out of books he loved, broken cars, trains, planes, boats, a drum bashed everywhere but on the skin, armless puppets, one-eyed teddys, a rubble of checkers, dominos, dice, playing cards, cookie crumbs, pennies, underwear, the overwhelming lagan of his rising, falling feelings. In this room the cat growled from low in her throat and darted without direction, up onto the bed, under the desk, soaring to the top of the dresser, double-timing into the closet, but never once disturbing the disarray.

I was less careful as I walked across the room. I recognized the shrill whirring motor of the record player. Round and round a record spun, the arm trembling on the ungrooved center of the disc.

The image of the three of them flashed in my mind, and I half sighed, half laughed, at how neatly the little one lay in his mother's lap. Overall the three comprised a hideously awkward corpus. But within the tangle of profiles and awful colors and the inhuman jam which sheathed her arms and the battered side of the seven-year-old's head, within this theatrically angled front-page picture lay an element of neat, sweet repose.

Whose wife was this? Whose children?

•

When I arrived home from work I found my wife had killed our two sons and taken her own life. My first thought was cruel and revealed to me a dark side of my nature that was even more shocking than the expressions on their faces.

Although I caught just a glimpse through the glass panes of the back door as I let myself in, I saw each one's face as if it were a masterpiece you run into all your life in books, in schools, in shops, on calendars, in ads, everywhere. The little one looked as if he had gone peacefully to sleep despite the agony of suffocation told by the bluish cast of his skin. The older boy had been screaming *Oh, No!* when death froze him forever. And my wife . . . the spike of pain which had contorted her every expression for so long was softened now by death. I saw the wishful, anxious innocence that had made me first fall in love.

Eventually I would act on that cruel thought. I knew myself well enough not to pretend it was a mistake and would go away by itself. But for the moment I drove it out of my head and poured myself a strong bourbon and water on the rocks. I drank it quickly, without tasting it or feeling it. Then I went to the phone and dialed my stepfather's number.

The tiny strung-together clicks separated as I released each number. I could hear every one distinctly enough to count them all, an auditory counterpart, I imagined, to seeing the individual dots in a photograph. They roared at me, echoing till I had to pull the receiver away. The picture broken into dots was on the front page of the local newspaper. I knew what the article would say, after having read so many like it and having worked one summer as a copy boy. I could write it myself: MOM KILLS KIDS/SELF. There would be speculation that the marriage was not going well, neighborly pronouncements about how nice she seemed, "Although we never really got to know her, they kept mostly to themselves." I'd cover the school angle, classmates, teachers, and I'd allow the fact that the older boy had a history of emotional and neurological problems to insinuate the motive. But, of course, all of it, every last word, would be only the journalistic truth. The real truth, if you believed the killer herself, was that she simply did not like her life, her children's lives, nor the lives they forced on one another.

Suddenly I realized that the phone had been ringing and ringing and my stepfather was not going to answer. With a shudder of panic I imagined them all—all my relatives and in-laws—standing on the breezeway paying one of their surprise visits. I even looked out the back door to make sure it was only panic. Sometimes they all came tumbling through that door, robbing my weekend, subduing me, forcing my wife out of her shell to cook dinner, to laugh at their anecdotes, to commiserate with their aches and pains. If they should arrive now, I would be the one forced out of a shell. I would have to be the perfect host, apologizing for my wife's indisposition, reminding them that kids are, after all, just kids. No matter Grandma and Grandpa came to see you. No matter Grandpa's leg is bad. A stolen Saturday or Sunday was less offensive when my wife's mother was alive. At least she entertained the children for hours and wore her unabashed devotion so openly that I could talk to her frankly, if kiddingly, about her frequent and interminable visits.

Her husband would begin wanting to go home an hour after they arrived, and she would want to plan the next visit the instant they finally left. It was a flabby love, to be sure, blind to every fault and built on nothing more substantial than her passion. I suppose her daughter and grandchildren were the only ones who returned her love in a way she could feel. I glanced at the bodies on the floor and knew that if there were a society of the dead, the three of them and Grandma were enjoying the last laugh, enjoying at last a visit which would never end.

I hung up the phone. Years from now, when I might be able to recollect everything that was happening this weekend with perfect clarity and understanding, I would know whether my dread of visitors on the breezeway was justified or only the first sign of the gradual, drunken, temporary loss of mind I might be experiencing. But no one must come, no one. Not my stepfather and mother, not my wife's stepmother and father. Not the milkman, the parcel post man, the newsboy, the oil man, the door-to-door salesman, the police . . .

The ringing of the phone made me jump. I made a quick bourbon and water while it rang. I stared at the black box, backed away from it. I even put my hand against it to feel the vibrations as a way to make doubly sure I wasn't imagining things.

Suddenly I heard all that there was to hear. The house and the neighborhood, triggered by the terrible rings of the phone, came blasting at me: the television in the den was playing; the pipes were gurgling; the cat was exercising her claws on a wicker chair; a truck came roaring around the curve of our road; next door the dog was running back and forth in the backyard, pulling its leash back and forth along the clothesline pulley.

And then a new sound disrupted all the others. It was the shock of my own voice.

"Hello," I said.

"Fine, Mom," I said.

"Good," I said.

"I was in the bathroom."

"I guess they're out having dinner," I said.

"I think Diane and her kid spent the day, maybe they all went out for something to eat," I lied.

I continued to lie.

I lied when I said I'll tell her to call you if she's not too tired. I lied when I said we'll probably see you Sunday. I lied when I re-assured her that everything was fine, really, your sixth sense must have misfired.

"Good-bye," I said.

"How's Ray's leg?" I asked, but she had already hung up.

"I wanted to know if he's up to a round of golf. I thought we'd make a day of it, just the two of us. Just the guys out in the sun, a few beers, I have a new putter I want to try out, and I figured we'd rent a motor cart; that way Ray won't have to walk . . ."

•

A coincidence will be my undoing, I felt. As passionately as I be-lieved that what belonged to me was mine to do with as I pleased (and that included my children, especially), I sensed that I would be blamed and punished for the murders on my dining room floor. I sensed also that my wife had had a similar notion when it hit her that she had taken back the two lives she had given. On the one hand, the two lives were completely, unarguably hers; but her friends and family and society at large would take the other view. Then, when she herself took the other view, she saved the world the trouble of pointing a finger and then pointing a gun at her head. But I was not about to kill myself; no undeniable guilt moved me in that direction.

I watched her now through the bottom of my bourbon glass and discovered that if I tipped it slightly the refraction in the thick glass made it look as if she were moving.

The coincidence of my thinking about her mother and then the phone call from my own mother at that exact moment was the sort of thing that worried me. Too difficult, too complicated to intercept or preempt all the surprises I might have to face. In the last year or two I was not up on my wife's daily routines. We each kept a certain part of our lives to ourselves, a private existence that was either none of the other person's business or decidedly uninteresting. Unlike other couples we knew, we had stopped exchanging the day-to-day trivia. So if she were expected somewhere tomorrow at one o'clock, I had no way of knowing. If her Avon lady were going to ring any minute, it would startle me. If her girlfriend suddenly showed up on the breezeway, tennis racket in hand, wondering where her partner was, I would have to return her serve as quick-wittedly as possible.

There was bound to be a detectable nervousness in one of my answers, a subsequent report, an investigation, a foolproof procedure of tracing this or that to me, me . . . and then what? Would the police burst through the back door and haul me off? And what about that pernicious, persistent thought I'd been trying to bury? When I could no longer control it and finally went out and did it, surely I would be leaving the door wide open to anyone with the least bit of suspicion.

Whatever solace I drew was from the complications. This was no simple family murder. They never are. It wasn't even a case of my wife's having been driven to the breaking point. There were subtle threads leading all ways that might never be completely untangled. Sometimes I thought I had the one thread that counted, only to find my theory knotted like a thick rope. I'd fall for the illusion and slide the knot down the thread until it vanished. But the thread no longer attached itself to anything.

I remembered being convinced two years ago when her mother died that if my wife were going to do something crazy, if ever she were to sink low enough to give up and let the quicksand texture of her life swallow her, it would have been then. The only other person who shared my wife's same fitful happinesses and increasing depression died an ironic death in the recovery room after open-heart surgery. The debilitating wages of her condition and the enormous trauma of the operation worked on her like a wrecking ball.

It was my wife's first brush with death, and I expected the worst. But the thread came loose, and she rose to all the painful occasions that ritualize death. She talked of a deep new understanding, of peaceful acceptance, of supernatural visitations late at night bathed in angelic light. But, again, the recovery was too much to bear. It would work at her in subtle ways, like a slow but inevitably fatal poison. The Waltons, Christmas, her father's quick remarriage, the older boy's first piano recital, the little one's first sentence, hearing others talk about their mothers . . . whether they were alive or dead did not matter.

I was vaguely aware of her crying jags, though she hid them like an animal hides its impending death. We knew we'd never find the spot our cat had chosen for her final resting place and joked about her toppling out of the medicine cabinet one morning with a bottle of sleeping tablets clutched in her paw.

But I knew where my wife went to cry. I just pretended not to.

And then I remembered the night she told me about the supermarket and how sure I was that it was over, the death of her mother had finally passed into that stony internal hump we all carry but learn to bear.

For several minutes, no matter where she went in the supermarket, she felt a stranger's eyes upon her. At last she caught an older woman staring, and was so bold as to go right up to her and ask if there was something wrong.

"No, no, please, forgive me," the older woman told my wife. "It's just that my daughter recently passed away, and there's something about you that reminds me of her."

Naturally my wife felt sorry that she had confronted the bereft mother so nastily, and she told me how she had apologized to the older woman for her little temper, and how she had said she understood because not long ago her mother had passed away.

She told me this much of the story in a voice that promised a more spectacular ending, and I hung on her every word. Vividly I pictured the aisles of the market, the lady; I crept into my wife's grief to fully appreciate this mystical fraternity of the abandoned whose members always seemed to find the eeriest ways of revealing themselves to one another.

Later, as my wife waited her turn in the checkout line, she realized that the older woman was directly in front of her. They smiled at each other, and then the older woman made her chilling request: "Would you do me a very big favor? When I'm about to leave, would you please say, 'Good-bye, Mom?'" Of course, she would understand if her request were too morbid for my wife, but it was apparent that the two words would mean a great deal to her.

"I told her I understood, and that I would do it, and that maybe it would even make me feel better about my mother," my wife had told me.

"She picked up her packages and turned to leave, and I choked out the words 'Good-bye, Mom.' It was like every tearjerker you ever saw rolled into one."

Just listening to this fairly astounding drama had begun to get to me, too.

"And then she disappeared out the door, and I guess being where I was, in the supermarket of all places, I was able to keep from bawling like a baby."

Still there was more. And the outraged look in my wife's eyes, her whole flabbergasted but triumphant attitude kept me on the edge of my chair. I thought of the fabulous Al Jolson spotlit in a cavernous Art Deco theater, the sweat pouring from his exhausted face, telling the folks to wait a minute, they ain't heard nothin' yet.

"I knew what I bought in the market," my wife had continued. "Ten, maybe fifteen dollars worth of meats and vegetables. But the checkout girl rang me up for thirty-seven dollars. 'There must be a mistake,' I said. The checkout girl looked confused. 'How does this come to thirty-seven dollars?' I asked her. 'It's all on one check,' she said at last. 'Your mother's groceries, too. She told me to put it all on your check.'"

Incredible. I remembered being absolutely stunned by the brilliance of the scheme, the shock to my wife, and the eerie luck of that damned woman to have picked out such a perfect, vulnerable mark.

"I was furious. The little one was with me, and I just left everything right on the checkout counter and yanked him out into the parking lot with me. Way on the other side, that sonofabitch was loading the last bundle into her Volkswagen, and the two of us ran like a couple of maniacs, slipping on the ice, dodging cars, crashing into little old ladies . . . but goddamnit if I was about to let that sonofabitch get away with it."

I was with her every step of the way by then.

"I got to her just as she was starting up the car. When she saw me, she lunged for the passenger door to lock it, but I managed to get it open first. She kicked at me, and I caught hold of her ankle with one hand and tried to keep my other hand on the hood of the little one's coat. Somehow she got the car started, but I knew she couldn't drive off if I held onto her leg. God, there I was, an ordinary housewife doing an ordinary little chore like going to the supermarket, and suddenly I'm lying in the snow holding onto a screaming kid with one hand and pulling with all my might on some woman's leg with my other hand and . . ."

"Jesus," I remembered screaming, "what the hell happened? Didn't you yell for help? Didn't you tell the checkout girl to get the manager?"

"I pulled. I kept pulling her leg as hard as I could . . . almost as hard as I'm pulling your leg right now."

Oh, yes. Loose threads. Many, many loose threads. I was still off balance from tugging at that one and having my wife snap it back at me. Just like all the others, it came from a wild ganglia and led nowhere. And yet murders do get solved, I nearly said aloud.

•

Was it so strange, after all, for me to be preoccupied with thoughts of self-preservation? Hadn't I survived a sad suburban story? Wouldn't well-wishers and sympathizers want me to put the pieces together and make a fresh start, and wasn't it true that no one would ever again begrudge me a little sliver of happiness or relief?

I went out into the backyard my wife had loved so much. Her garden was plotted. The moon danced in the rippling ballroom of our aboveground pool. Next door the dog raced its pulley back and forth.

There in the dark and rustling coolness it began to sink in. Her tragic life began to make intolerable sense to me. Everything she had ever said or done had meant something, although I had been and still tried to be—more than ever—distrustful of any significance. Nothing is significant, was my slogan. Everything goes away sooner or later. And, in fact, the three of them had gone away.

It was dark enough to take off all my clothes without the neighbors seeing, and I lowered myself into the four feet of water, upsetting the moon and the overhanging branches of our white pine as I broke into the still surface skin. Round and round I waded, shivering from the waist up, vaguely aware that my genitals were shriveling. The little rounded extra weight I was carrying on my stomach seemed exaggerated by the waterline. "Don't," she pleaded with me whenever I overate, "men your age get heart attacks and I don't want to be left alone with the kids, I couldn't cope with that. Nothing could be worse."

Round and round, inventorying her many complaints: I haven't got a minute to myself; there isn't anything I can do without being interrupted; they exasperate me, taunt me, beat me down; one thinks he's smarter than I am and uses me to sharpen his wits, the other one hardly thinks at all and gives in to every one of his feelings no matter how destructive or embarrassing or disruptive or dangerous; sometimes I wonder if I really love them the way every mother is supposed to love her children; it never goes away, never, all I can think about is that the older they get the later I'm going to have to let them stay up; if I have to mop up spilled apple juice one more time I'll kill myself; no, it never goes away, never; my mother looked at the problems I have with my children as still another problem she was having with me; why can't he be like other boys; why can't I be like other mothers? On and on, round and round, numb underwater, tense and tight and galvanized in the night air.

So she killed them and that was that. And she killed herself for good measure.

I gazed into the water and saw the image of the three of them on the dining room floor. Wherever I walked they followed. Wherever they followed the moon came, too. And then I saw myself, dressed up in a sport jacket and open-collar shirt, combing my hair, studying the real me as if *I* were the mirror, and then my image left to do a cruel, dark thing.

.

When I arrived home from work I found my wife had killed our two sons and taken her own life. The room seemed to fill up with an insufferable heat, and I ran gasping to our aboveground pool. I tore off my clothes and jumped into the water. At first I walked around thinking of God knows what, trying to make some sense out of it all. Finally I submerged myself and swam beneath the water until my lungs were ready to burst.

Leaving my clothes behind on the shadowy deck, my wallet still in my back pocket, I made my way slowly back to the house. Halfway home I stepped on one of the kids' toys, and the pain stabbed me throughout my naked body.

I wondered if I were undergoing some kind of emotional shock or temporary lunacy. After letting myself in again through the wide-open back door, I closed it, locked it, shut off the breezeway light, noted that I must have already turned off the stove and doused the smoking black chili pot. I walked purposefully through the dining room, around the three bodies, into the den. I settled my soaking wet body into the chair facing the television set. Kojak was just coming on.

"Did you touch anything?" he asked, trying to keep his celebrated gruffness under control.

"It's just a suicide. She killed the kids and slashed her wrists because she couldn't take it anymore. I can tell you anything you want to know."

"Yeah, well, tell me this, bay-bee," pointing his lollipop at my face, "what if it wasn't suicide, what about murder and like that?"

Someone very carefully chalked the outline of the three bodies, and when the bodies were finally removed, after pictures and samples and scrapings and dustings, the outline was a puzzle piece, as amorphous and unrecognizable as the real meaning of death.

"All right, tell me," the lieutenant said, gesturing for me to follow him into the kitchen, into the bathroom, the den, upstairs, wherever he needed to snoop. "Any enemies?"

No one ever hated her. She had always been too meek to offend people, although recently she had been looking out more for herself, probably as a result of the pointless suffering she watched her mother endure and then the cold quickness with which so many friends and relatives (Daddy chief among them) had packed away her mother's memory. Nor were there any jealous, spurned, psychopathic old beaus.

She kidded me about the parcel post delivery man's good looks, and one day he did show up on the breezeway with no packages after my wife had unwittingly encouraged him on his last visit by assuming he would enjoy hearing that she kidded me. And there was a rather creepy TV repairman who paid an emergency call one night and brought along a friend. They were both Hungarian or something, and while the repairman struggled up on the roof with the antenna, the friend, who was merely along for the ride, made himself comfortable in the den. He switched the TV from the Muppets, which the kids were watching, to a horror movie.

The little one ran and told my wife, and she had to tell the Hungarian to leave the Muppets on. I was outside making sure the ladder was secure, and later, after the set was fixed and the two men had gone and the kids were sleeping, my wife told me that she thought the "friend" had burned a cigarette hole in our Oriental rug, but she wasn't positive and, besides, if we just shaved the thick pile a bit, you couldn't see the burn unless you knew it was there.

I was beginning to feel that there were a lot of things to see if only you knew they were there. But surely the parcel post man and the strangely at-home Hungarian were not killers.

Of course, I had absolutely no way of knowing if there were any psychopathic beaus . . . I could not account for my wife's every daytime adventure. I believed she was loyal to me and timid with other men and mostly satisfied with the love I showed her. And yet the logic of that was all wrong. If she did kill herself, she could hardly have been satisfied. And if she hadn't been satisfied, she might have searched for satisfaction in all sorts of hellholes. In which case murder was not out of the question. In which case I was not off the hook.

I had the same feeling I had had the other week on the train going to work: I was a toy then—like one of my little boy's Weebles—and an enormous childlike force had dropped me in my town, put my house nearby, set down a train and tracks a few inches away, given me a car, a subway, several crowded New York City streets, and, finally, at the other end of this Tinkertoy world, put me on the thirty-eighth floor of a forty-story office building. Now that same childlike force had just dropped me in my chair, put three corpses in the next room, set Kojak on my trail, sprinkled clues about the house, sealed the exits, and finally, it had abandoned me the way I'd seen my little one suddenly lose interest after spending an intense fifteen minutes constructing the world out of thick, plain blocks.

Kojak was looking at me impatiently, suspiciously. In the back of my mind was the irrational fear that he knew more than I did about the killings. And adding to that fear was the realization that every single time Kojak smelled a rat, a rat showed up.

"I'm gonna tell you something you're not going to like," he said, sniffing at the caked black chili. "I don't think your wife did this. I think she was murdered and your kids were murdered and the killer made it look like suicide and like that. And if I'm right, then you're going to be finding out a lot about your wife you don't want to know. But I'll tell you this," he pointed his thumb at his heart and spoke with his special admixture of tenderness and accusation, "I want to know."

Back at headquarters, there was mutinous chatter about a new departmental regulation which made it tougher to police the city. The death of a typical American family, the researching of its aching lives up to the final disintegration, was obviously not compelling enough to preoccupy the Nielsons for sixty minutes straight. When my wife and children became too unbearable or too boring, there was now a thin subtexture of political handcuffing to cut to, an uncomplicated melodrama of big city cops who were being kept from protecting the people by the people themselves. And yet somehow, I knew, the case would get solved. Someone's sure hand was putting the investigation on track. One cop was going to follow up on the Hilo Lounge matchbook found on the kitchen floor. Another was going to make inquiries around town. A third was in direct communication with the coroner's lab, awaiting scientific proof that the depth of the razor slashes on my wife's wrists could not have been self-inflicted. Kojak himself was on his way to my mother and stepfather's house.

•

Ray's house was just like all the others in the development, small, white, treeless, dismal. Kojak's car pulled in behind my mother's in the short, narrow drive. Its rear end stuck out into the quiet street.

My stepfather answered the door. He spoke and dressed and walked like someone trying to get used to retirement, inviting Kojak in with two weary waves of his pipe-holding hand. Then he limped into the living room where my mother was up on her feet instantly, a withered coil of worry ready to spring at the casual lieutenant at the first hint of trouble.

"I just want to ask you some questions about your son," he said, failing to calm her down.

As ready as my mother was to crack, it was Ray who was my worry. His face was haunted as if it possessed some scandalous secret. He could not hide it, although he tried. His wildly colored shirt was a shock in the sedately decorated room. He relit his pipe and filled the stale air with a wreath of aromatic whiteness. As he limped to the far side of the room, his slippers slapped along the bare floor. He could not make himself invisible. One glance at Ray, and Kojak would be on him like a wolf pack, snarling questions from every direction, spitting accusations, innuendos, sinking a hundred teeth into my stepfather's every whimpering admission.

But for the moment the lieutenant stayed with my mother, asking her if she knew of any trouble between my wife and me.

"Trouble? My God, they were childhood sweethearts. From the time they were kids all they wanted to do was get married."

The minute I saw her I loved her with a love far older than we were. In fact the story of our marriage was how I spent the next twenty-odd years trying to grow into my feeling for her. But it always kept one step, one word, one deed ahead of me.

At twenty I thought physical passion was the way, and we drained our loins like wild monkeys. I meant to have her devour me as proof that I loved her.

Ray stuck his pipe into the middle of his secret and spouted three sweet clouds.

At twenty-five I thought responsibility was the answer. I would become a man, complete with a good job, a reliable future, a house, life insurance; I would be a pillar for my wife to lean on, hide behind, show off, embrace. Whatever success I achieved would be hers. I would work for her, dedicate my brains and brawn to her exalted position as queen of our two-bee hive.

"He tells me he works for a research company."

"He's a vice-president. My son is the whole company, if you want to know."

"Yeah, I'm sure he is. Must work hard, huh? Long hours, weekends, trips, like that?"

"Yes," my mother said, trying to appear proud, remembering it was during a week I was away that my wife spent seventeen deliriously painful hours giving birth to our first child.

"What does she do when he's away? I mean, does she stay at home or go out or what? What do you think she does with her free time?"

When work began stealing me away, I thought having children was the answer. The one of us that is the two of us. A living symbol of the closeness I could never adequately express. We did not stop to think if we were suited to the roles of parents, we just plunged in, genitals first.

The nine months passed like nine years. I was completely unable to share in my wife's private joy. It was not happening to me. There was no bulge in my stomach, no little limbs kicking me awake at night. Try as we might, I could not understand her mysterious smile any more than she could understand my polite one.

And so I gave up. I steeped myself in a new research project that kept me at the office late and on weekends. It took me on several overnight and four week-long business trips. But, most importantly, it gave me a secret. A joy. A fullness thereof. For six months I truly was, as my mother had boasted, the whole company, if you want to know.

"Really, Lieutenant, you know we women hardly know the meaning of free time." My mother tried flirting.

What was he getting at? Did he really think my wife led some kind of double life? Doubly depressing, maybe. Doubly enslaved to what she believed her children's needs demanded of her. Doubly futile, as it turned out. But the image of her baring one heaving breast in Shantytown after dropping the kids off at school was something only a cop who had seen everything would come up with.

"All I know, ma'am, is that your daughter-in-law and your grandchildren are dead, and I want to make sure nobody's got any questions I can't answer."

She's shocked. She didn't know. Ray's mouth is open.

"Now what I'm trying to find out is if your daughter-in-law ever engaged in any extracurricular activity and like that bip bop." Kojak was getting angry.

"Dead?"

"You mean nobody told you? Sonny Boy didn't let you know?"

My mother rushed into the middle of a wrenching, throbbing, shrieking hysteria. Her eyes rolled in her head, her hands fluttered, her body seemed to grope for a comforting place to collapse in. Ray was not that place. He knew he was once removed from the inner circle of the family and stayed along the sidelines, nearby if needed, not able to intrude.

"She had no idea," he said, and I wondered whether he was still playing the part of the second husband or if he had meant by the word "she" that somehow *he* had known. He knew something, that was obvious.

"My babies . . . ohhh . . . my God . . . what am I going to do . . . let me die . . . my babies . . ." Among the ranting sobs a coherence was beginning to emerge, and Kojak sensed that if he hung around my mother a little longer she might reveal something worthwhile.

A merciless close-up of my mother's agonized face caught me by surprise. I saw in through her wild eyes and contorted open mouth to a flaming family album she kept in the darkness of her mind. The wretchedness of her motherhood resided there. The choking words Kojak was ready to write down in his crumpled little notebook were also afire.

But I could trust my mother. Even half-insane she would not speak against me. Some instinct deep within would prevent her from revealing the horrors I could see through her eyes. My mother was, after all, my mother. She would throw her body in front of a train for me. She would stand a thousand tortures without accusing me. My wife's children were not so lucky, but I had the will and flesh of this steel mother to protect me, despite the angry flames crackling in her white, old head.

"Lieutenant."

The urgency in Ray's voice finally pulled the camera from my mother's face to his.

"It may be none of my business, Lieutenant, but my wife's son . . ."

"I'm listening, bay-bee."

There was a sharp blast, the instantaneous sound of glass shattering, and the actor who was speaking grabbed his neck as he fell to the floor.

•

I liked Ray. He married my mother when she needed a man most—after losing one—and the marriage succeeded beyond the emergency of its beginning.

I was twelve, too old to accept Ray as a real father but too young to see him as merely a husband. We respected each other the way men under fire do. Both of us felt responsible for my mother, the motherland. And the battle was won so easily, my mother recovered and was happy so quickly, that Ray and I could share the fruits of our victory without jealousy.

I had been the infantry, marching through the hospital corridors leading to my real father's death, bearing a corner of his casket through the rainy cemetery, pacing the foyer outside my mother's bedroom, bellying in beneath her covers, holding up, managing a smile through the dirt of the trenches, giving her inspiration. And then Ray Spaulding parachuted into our no-man's-land like some great, godly dove of peace. He dealt the enemy within its final, crushing blow.

Together we celebrated a new peacefulness. We went on vacation, their honeymoon, and lay in a sun that never did us harm. We moved into a new house, the one I hate now for its small, white likeness to all the others in the development. But I liked it then.

For the first time I had a room of my own, a secret sanctum where I could discover what being myself was like. No adults intruded with their adult ideas of what becoming an adult required of me.

After school, when my schoolmates ran around, and after bedtime, when they lay recharging their bodies for tomorrow's tussles, I roamed the splendid isolation of my room. There as both performer and audience I created the world. True love was the feeling I commanded from head to toe as I masturbated into the middle of the night and dreamt my pillow was my wife-to-be. Understanding was a poem quickly scribbled into a secret notebook. All knowledge was simply being alone so that no one and nothing could challenge the things I believed.

It occurred to me that I still lived in that bedroom, that wherever I have gone I have taken it with me. I closed my eyes and saw it so clearly: the rose-colored walls; the purple coverlet; the restricted view of outside from between the shuttered bottom half of my window and the valanced top; the oval rug with its concentric rings of warm, fleshy browns and pinks; the full-length mirror on the inside of the door; another mirror, set inside a replicated captain's wheel, hanging over the dresser.

"He's dead," Kojak announced.

But I knew Ray was not dead, only dying. Nicotine poisoning had cost him three toes so far, and the doctors were beginning to speculate that an amputation to the knee might be the only answer.

Yet Ray continued to smoke two packs a day besides the three or four pipes he'd light to wean himself off cigarettes.

Slowly, he was destroying himself. He was devouring his own body with each obsessive puff.

If he knew he was dying, and of course he did, then what would keep him from talking? And what did he know? And why was I afraid? The look on his face had been frightened as well as frightening, as if whatever he knew would expose himself along with me. As if just knowing implicated him in the horror.

"Look at his shirt," Kojak beamed to one of his men. "Notice anything funny?"

"Only that I wouldn't be caught dead wearing it."

"Hey. Comedian. Look at the nice palm trees and like that, huh. It's Hawaiian, bay-bee. And guess what nice, sweet, thoughtful little boy who has made several *business* trips to Howareya and no doubt has sipped a Mai Tai or two in a certain Hilo Lounge of matchbook fame went and gave this nice shirt with the pretty palm trees to the dearly departed over here? Yeah. I think maybe I better have another little chitchat with Sonny Boy, hum."

Once they start they never leave you alone. They're at you all the time until they finally break you down. Didn't they see that that's why my wife killed herself? The kids were at her—at her—at her like a machine gun. Even when they were out of the house, sticky floors and unmade beds and clogged toilets and strewn-about clothes and supper plans and a thousand and one unavoidable reminders of their inescapable presence were at her at her at her all the time, gunning her down, sniping at her, breaking her will.

The consensus of opinion would be that she finally lost her grip. But I was not so sure. Was it really crazy to do what one had to do to get rid of the pain? Was it any less crazy to pinch the skin on your thigh in order to take your mind off a relentless, torturous headache? I suppose what I was asking myself was whether or not misery is the natural, normal state of man. If it is, then yes, my wife had acted quite insane on two accounts: one, for not having recognized it, and two, for not having accepted it.

•

The bourbon was beginning to have an effect on me. I could not otherwise explain why I should think of Mrs. P. sitting so stoically at the far end of the table. When the moderator had finally coaxed an innermost thought from Mrs. P., the reaction on our side of the one-way mirror was uproarious.

The two representatives from the advertising agency howled with laughter. The man who wanted to know how to market his ingenious contraceptive device smacked his forehead with his open hand and said "I don't believe it" over and over again. I had been too pre-occupied with the flow and mechanics of the research project to react. But now Mrs. P.'s remark about women jolted me as if I were hearing it for the first time.

"Women don't have orgasms," she had said, "they just satisfy their husbands."

What made the statement so shocking was not its untruthfulness, but the simple, almost defiant belief with which Mrs. P. had di-vulged her personal truth. Her face had been so calm as she spoke to no one in particular. She might as well have been alone in the carefully designed blandness of the room.

I remembered having guessed her age and husband's occupation incorrectly and having wanted to touch the silken silver gray of the Virginia Slims Jump Jacket she wore. Under her left breast were stitched the words "You've come a long way, baby." Someone on our side of the mirror said that was a laugh considering how far back her stupid statement took her. At the time I felt a pang of resentment, but I kept quiet because these people were my clients.

Afterwards, as we all nibbled on the roast beef sandwiches I had provided and discussed our preliminary findings, Mrs. P.'s statement came up again. One of the advertising people, a woman, was trying to square the effects of the media in her own mind. How, she won-dered, could a few cigarette commercials convince Mrs. P. that she had come a long way, and yet a thousand newspaper articles, count-less TV interviews, hundreds of books, and thousands of stories in all the women's magazines had failed to teach her that not only was she able to have an orgasm, she was gooddamn well entitled to have one? Again I wanted to speak but held myself back. I thought I knew the answer. I thought I knew Mrs. P.

Maybe it was because I was in the business of gathering raw, emotional information that her statement had a kind of dignity to it. Somehow I could understand the Mrs. P.'s and their convictions, and

I never judged either harshly. The Mrs. P.'s were the ones who judged. That was the whole point of a focus group interview, to focus on the judgments of the group members, to focus on them through a one-way mirror while the group's moderator presented an ad campaign or a package design or a new product or a model's face or a chemist's formula or whatever else needed a quick splash of research.

Obviously, Mrs. P. was in my thoughts because of my wife and the children. I knew her the same way I knew them, I realized. For all these years I had watched my wife and then our children through my one-way mirror. I had studied them, loved them, bestowed upon them the special dignity that is the right of those who don't know they're being watched.

The cat stirred on top of the television, where she had been stretched out in one of her comical, twitching, deeply unconscious naps. She always picked the noisiest spot to go to sleep.

She jumped down with a thud and a grunt and took herself to her litter box. A few moments later she was back. I watched her as she lay back against the baseboard to begin her bath. What a strange breed, I thought to myself, as she ran her rough tongue up and down her belly. She was not really a friendly cat and yet she needed to be with people. When she was with us she'd act aloof and independent and yet she was always where we were. You'd think she'd go to sleep in another room. You'd think she'd lick and chew at her private parts where we couldn't see her.

As if she had read my mind, she suddenly left off and stared back at me. One second. Two seconds. Three seconds. And then her head darted back down between her spread hind legs to finish the job.

Everywhere she licked her fur it was wet and sleek and matted. But by the time she went on to a new section, the fur she had just cleaned was fluffy again. I wondered if my older boy's head, where the blood had matted his hair, would be dry now; if his blond hair would fall silkily over an unmangled ear.

•

The Volunteer Rescue Squad siren sounded through the darkness outside. On and on it wailed. Kojak seemed to cut the noise of that siren as his car screeched to a stop and he cut the noise of his siren.

The house was empty, drawers and closets flung open to give the obvious impression that someone had just been there and left in a hurry. One of my cigarettes was smoldering in an ashtray; it made me want to light another one.

The lieutenant smelled blood; he raced back outside to his car radio and ordered an APB. The chirrupy little voice on the other end told him that he better get downtown quick, the captain had to see him right away.

"Yeah, well, tell the captain I got more important things to do than fan his sweaty little brow just because the commissioner's putting the heat on. Oh, and listen, bay-bee, put it in your own very kind words, would you do that for me?"

"Wait, Lieutenant," the voice cricketed, "it's not that. It's the slash case, the dead girl's mother-in-law is down here and she just filled up a whole notebook."

"Well, what do you know?"

A spider walked across the television screen, making me realize how far away from the actual surface of the screen the moving images were. Each time it set down one of its hairlike feet it pinpointed the inch or more of glass between what I saw and what there was to be seen.

I believe my mother thought she was throwing her body in front of a train to protect me. Fully in control of herself, she sat erect and proper in the manner of a fading Victorian beauty. Very deliberately, she repeated to Kojak the story of my wife.

She told how at the start of our marriage my wife had given up any thought of a career, although she was very bright and had won a fellowship to do postgraduate work in biology. Instead, my mother rattled on like a practiced narrator, she took a job at the college to supplement my negligible starting salary in the research department of a large food corporation. She became a secretary in the biology department, handling all the paperwork for the chairman and thinking it was better than ordinary office work because she was in her own element. She was surrounded by the texts of her major interest, in contact with students, close to the teachers, and earning money besides. The truth of the matter was that instead of keeping up with biological abstracts or arguing theory with hotheaded seniors or talking shop during a professor's free period, she spent most of her time experimenting with the way she looked. Every evening she would arrive home with a different shade of nail polish, a new hairdo, another cheap bauble from the five-and-dime.

It was clear, to my mother at least, that my wife's heart was no longer in the biology department, and that in fact just being there day after day was having a "funny" effect on her.

It wasn't until she quit her job that I realized what that funny thing was. A man, of course. Well, a boy, in this case. A sophomore with an almost indistractible dedication to DNA and a great wild shock of the blondest hair. He was big and handsome and full of himself, and the fact that she was married made her the most desirable woman on earth in his raw blue eyes.

Fortunately he was young enough not to mind making a fool of himself. Every day he hung around her desk in the biology department. He'd steal her lunch bag, set a match to the paper in her typewriter, beg her to have a beer with him, ask what she thought of a preposterous DNA theory, threaten to kill himself if she didn't go to bed with him, give her presents which she couldn't bring home, little tokens of his affection that he made himself. The bottom drawer of her desk, way in the back where it was dark and you had to grope to find anything, was filled with mawkish poems, handmade valentines, inscribed stones, and a crazy bouquet of weeds and string and colored tissues and bald dandelions. It was all so cute and amusing and at the same time so simple and real.

"My God, you're building me a nest," she half joked when he presented her with that bouquet. Just clutching the bouquet to her bosom puffed her up like a bird.

And yet what he accomplished with all this attention was exactly the opposite of what he hoped for. She rededicated herself to her marriage with more loyalty and love than any man could understand. Not out of fear or self-doubt. But to return the compliment the entire male kingdom was paying her in the person of one very charming, very handsome, very innocent sophomore.

The hairdos, the makeup, the earrings—I remember she even had her ears pierced—they were all for her husband. Look at me, she was saying, look at me this way, that way, every possible way. I'm desirable. I'm beautiful. A boy with the body of a statue and hair the color of youth and eyes that are not afraid of mine wants me. But I'm yours. All yours.

Finally she quit her job at the biology department so she could be home constantly. She studied cookbooks and clipped interior decorating tips from all the women's magazines. The apartment was ridiculously small, the kitchen especially, but she worked long and hard at turning our home into a showplace and meals into exotic feasts. And still she found time to design and redesign her face and body.

One night when her underpants were slipped below her hips, a bright gold star shone on her abdomen. Another night illuminated a fresh shave where her pubic hair had been. False nails one early evening. Theatrical eyes one morning. A bikini one wintry Saturday afternoon, only after losing twelve pounds and then regaining three.

"It's all so shamefully perverse, Lieutenant," an old woman said to Kojak.

•

It was my first business trip, a learning trip, to Buffalo. Several women were going to be asked to talk about a jelly-filled dough that you pop into a toaster. They had all been screened to qualify for the interview according to age, income, and the presence of young children.

In the first group there were ten women, and I stared at each one very intently through the one-way mirror. Larraine, I still recall her name, came right up to the glass to fix her makeup during the five minutes or so when everyone was still arriving. I could not take my eyes off her.

She was older looking than the age she had written on one of our research forms, and tired looking, too. Too much makeup too sloppily applied drew more attention to the unmade parts of her large, already wrinkling face. Her hair was reddish blond, brassy really, with stray wisps going in all directions.

As she contorted her mouth to make it accept new layer upon layer of pale pink lipstick, I found her looking directly into my face, although she could not see it. If the mirror had not been there we could have kissed each other. But unaware that her mirror was staring back at her, she went on mugging and making monkey faces.

I was becoming unnerved by her. Not having gone into the observation room beforehand to see with my own eyes if the one-way mirror was detectable, I thought for an instant that perhaps she *could* see me and was putting on her show just to make me uneasy.

But as much as I wanted to turn away, the unconscious image of her grotesquely close face was too fascinating to give up.

I started to light a cigarette. Suddenly her eyes darted toward the flare of the match. Everyone on my side of the mirror yelled at once to put out the match, that that was the one thing that could be seen through the glass. But I knew it was too late. All through the session Larraine kept looking at the mirror, waiting for another spark to reveal the faces of voyeurs.

Finally she asked the moderator if the mirror was one-way, and he proved how good a moderator he was by casually admitting that he needed one highly skilled hidden observer to pick up the nonverbal responses of the women. This observer was like an auctioneer's spotter, he explained, in case Larraine should gesture rather than speak into the recording system which had never been kept secret.

The moderator's answer seemed to satisfy her, although she immediately stared at us for a few seconds, and I sensed her bewilderment at not being able to see the face she knew was looking back at her.

Nor could the sophomore see my wife's face as she opened the peephole and saw his distorted good looks.

As near as I can figure, the blond kid rang the bell just about the time I had struck the match.

When my wife asked what he wanted, my mother reported, the innocent-looking sophomore told her he had a message from the chairman, not to worry, let him in for a minute, and then he laughed at their formality and said, "Hey, how ya been, anyway?"

It put her at ease to see his broad smile and bright eyes through the peephole. Though she doubted that he had any message from the chairman, her own good judgment of character convinced her it was silly to be so suspicious, and her afternoon boredom—especially since there was to be no end to it that night or for three more days until I came home from Buffalo—convinced her that it was silly to turn away a bit of unexpected amusement.

She let him in, asking how he was, if he wanted a cup of coffee, what was happening in the biology department, before she even got the door closed.

"Good; no, thanks; nothing much," he answered, and they both laughed away some nervousness.

He began to look around the tiny apartment, always facing his hostess, moving sideways and backwards, and he kept his hands behind his back. Noticing this, she suspected that he had brought her another one of his crazily romantic gifts—perhaps another bouquet of dandelions and weeds and string and pink and blue tissues.

"What have you got behind your back?" she asked coyly.

Thrusting his hands toward her suddenly, fingers spread stiffly apart, he smiled a smile she had never seen before and snarled, "Nothing."

The word seemed to ring on and on in the little room.

Abruptly the entire mood changed. The sophomore walked up to my wife and looked at her very slowly, stopping at her hips to muse aloud that this was how she dressed during the day. From the expression on his face it was evident that he liked her very lightweight pants and the man's white dress shirt she had on and the tiny silver earrings shaped like teardrops.

The kettle whistled in the kitchen, and she asked again if he'd like a cup of coffee. But instead of answering, he went to the stove himself, took off the kettle, and found a cup draining next to the sink.

She was afraid to aggravate the unfamiliar swing in the sophomore's personality, so she said nothing as he searched the cupboard for instant coffee and then the silverware drawer for a teaspoon and then the cupboard again for the sugar bowl.

"So this is where you keep things," he said, adding milk to the coffee. "This is what you do each time you want a cup of coffee." And then he handed her the cup, gesturing that he had made it for her.

"What do you want?" she finally asked.

He spun around, thrusting his hands at her again, fingers wide apart.

"Nothing."

His innocent face suddenly took on an ominousness. The very same expression which had flattered and amused her in the past suddenly became threatening. The physical sophomore no longer bore any resemblance to the emotional sophomore. Somehow it would have been less terrifying if he had had dark, evil eyes and a jagged scar and muddy prison clothes. He would have seemed less out of control.

"This must be your closet," he smiled, pointing to the one closet in the one-and-a-half-room apartment.

He opened the closet and took down the long pink nightgown that was hanging on a hook inside the door. He asked her if this was what she had slept in last night, and when she nodded her head, he tossed it to her and told her to put it on.

She fought back the panic and tried to foresee what he was planning.

"What do you mean, put it on?" she tried an annoyed little laugh.

Without raising his voice he said, "Do it," so that the words became the most horrible threat.

At that moment she knew she had to decide whether to go along with him or risk a fate far more terrible than putting on her nightgown. It was clear that he knew I was away, my mother had told me, and that the sophomoric advances he had always made had meant more to him than my wife had thought, and that he wanted something very specific from her, otherwise why hadn't he attacked her as soon as he was in the door? Perhaps, she thought, he will not hurt me. Perhaps the best thing to do is humor him to keep myself from real danger.

"Can I go into the bathroom to put it on?"

"Is that where you went last night?"

"Yes."

"Well, sure. Sure, go into the bathroom." He led the way. He opened the bathroom door for her. He turned on the light. And then he sat down on the edge of the tub to watch.

Like a frightened little girl she asked, "Are you going to rape me?"

He motioned for her to put on the nightgown.

She wanted to turn her back to him, but she was afraid. Turning three-quarters away, she saw that she could complete the turn and see his image reflected in my shaving mirror on the bamboo shelf over the toilet. She stared unblinkingly into the round glass as she unbuttoned her white shirt. When it was off and her back was exposed to the sophomore, she watched his reflected face to see if it was going to drool or if its eyes were going to spin like pinwheels. But his expression barely changed. His eyes were fixed on all of her at once, it seemed, and his smile, without physically changing, grew more like the one she remembered from lunchtime at the biology department.

Instead of taking her pants right off, she decided to slip the nightgown over her head and bare back first and then undo the belt, buttons, and zipper of her pants. This contrived modesty didn't seem to faze the rapt sophomore. Stiffly she dropped her pants and the hem of her nightgown simultaneously, stepping out of the crumpled lightweight chinos with the usual lack of gracefulness.

The nightgown was a flimsy polyester, and you could see shadows of her body through it wherever the material hung loosely.

"Do you sleep in your underpants?"

She thought she said yes too quickly, but again it didn't faze him. He left the bathroom and gallantly prepared her bed by removing the bolsters from the hide-a-bed couch, folding out the skeletal springs and skinny mattress, and spreading the blanket he remembered seeing on a top shelf in the clothes closet. Two pillows were also on the shelf, and the sophomore took one, plumped it up, and put it at the head of the bed.

Unfolded, the bed took up most of the little room. The sophomore sat on the edge of a soft armchair, his elbows on his knees, the heels of his palms supporting either side of his jawbone.

"I'm waiting," he said, and the action of his jawbone lifted his head up on each syllable.

The sophomore was waiting for her to get into bed, watching for her to inch past him, to brush against him as she took the only logical route to the frighteningly immense bed.

But she climbed over the arm of the couch to avoid him and bounced safely into a sitting position. She drew her legs in under her, stretching the nightgown like a tent from her shoulders to her knees. Through the taut sheer material her breasts were blurry but visible, the tensed nipples standing out vividly in the polyester haze.

"Is that how you sit late at night when you're watching television?" the sophomore asked, staring at her breasts, making them tingle with his wide-eyed gaze, bobbing his head on every syllable.

Before she could answer, he closed the blinds and turned off every light and knelt on the floor beside her.

"What?" she whimpered.

"Nothing." And his spread fingers flew out again in the semidarkness.

"Just lie down, close your eyes."

She could hardly close her eyes, for he was close enough at that point so that she could hear his breathing. Except it wasn't breathing. It was more pronounced and irregular. He was smelling her.

She did lie down; after all, she had done everything else he had asked without suffering bodily harm, so why should she draw the line at lying down? But her amazement kept her eyes open as she watched the top of his wavy blond head move the length of her body and heard his deep inhalations at several points—at her neck, under her arm, her hip, every few inches along her leg, her foot. Then he covered her up and stood over her.

"All right. Morning," he announced suddenly, and drew open the blinds. "Time to get up."

For a fleeting moment she thought the game might be over, that she might laugh and tell him he really had her going, now what about that cup of coffee. But she couldn't be sure until he laughed first, and there was no sign from him that the perverse paces he was putting her through were finished quite yet. There was still a direct insistence in the tone of his voice and cold steel in the way he motioned for her to do his bidding.

"Put away the bed."

He watched her every movement as she obeyed, paying as much attention to the bones of her planted feet as he did to her face. He walked all around her, crouching, bending into her, beside her, over her, around and around like a fashion photographer, snapping the ephemeral folds of her gown with his eyes, the tiny movements of her face, the various angles of her body as she bent and extended and bent again along with the collapsing, disappearing hide-a-bed.

He got down on the floor for a closer look at her feet as she stood on her toes to put the pillow and cover back up on the closet shelf, and she nearly caught a piece of his head when she dropped suddenly back onto her heels.

"Good," he said, rolling onto his back and pulling wide the skirt of her nightgown so he could take a playful peek up her legs as long as she was standing over him. It was the kind of juvenile action she had come to expect of the old sophomore, not the present one, and she allowed herself to think maybe her lovesick suitor was reseizing control of her deranged invader. She held her nightgown to her thighs to keep it from ballooning out, and he leaped to his feet at the rebuff.

"Why so modest? You're going to take it all off now anyway, aren't you? It's time for your shower."

He pointed at the bathroom, led the way, flicked on the light, flung aside the shower curtain, and turned on the water, which blurted down from the shower head in one thick rope before thinning out into a fine spray. He stood there with his hand on the faucet, his arm under the shower, the water soaking through the sleeve of his plaid shirt. A second shower, noisier and angrier, poured from his elbow.

If she were going to continue to humor him, she would have no choice but to undress. Looking into his eyes to see how close he might be to making her obey, she could hear herself silently screaming for me, praying I would come crashing through the front door. She realized she had not actually confronted the sophomore, had not refused any of his demands, and quickly she tried to predict what his reaction would be if she simply walked out of the steaming bathroom. As if to answer her thought, he kicked the door shut and tilted his head ever so slightly, like a bowler beginning his approach. The concentration in his face was frightening as he commanded her to get into the shower.

Blindly, sweating, as fast as she possibly could, she took off her nightgown and then her underpants and stepped in under the relentless water. She turned her back to the sophomore and folded her arms across her chest, but he grabbed her hip and spun her around so that she faced him, and she had to unfold her arms to keep from losing her balance.

Although she was standing stark naked in front of him, the water running seductively onto her breasts, beading at the tight, goose-pimply nipples, dripping crookedly from her newly regrown but still sparse pubic hair, the sophomore stared at her face.

"Wash up," he said cheerfully.

He never even noticed the jaundiced droplets that broke through the pubic dam and relieved her of uncontrollable terror.

Dutifully she lathered a big sponge mitt and began to soap her body. Only then did he draw his intense gaze from her face to wherever she moved the mitt.

As before, he seemed to be looking at the entire scene, even while concentrating on a single part of her.

She hurried through the shower, trying to drive away his presence by surrendering all senses to the heat and sound and torrent of the jets. She closed her eyes to make herself invisible and faced into the rush of water, standing like that for several long moments, letting the cascading shower wash away the soap.

Then all of a sudden the water stopped.

He did everything suddenly, making every premeditated move seem as though he had just thought of it.

There were little drops of water in her eyes that she had to rub away before she could see what the sophomore was doing. He was not leering at her naked body as she feared, but rummaging through the medicine cabinet for all the powders, ointments, creams, instruments, wands, sticks, puffs, brushes, and whatever else was obviously hers. After laying them all out on the edge of the sink, he turned to her shivering body and asked why she didn't dry herself off.

She made a sarong of the large bath towel he threw her and dried her hair with the smaller hand towel. Her hairdo then was short, almost in spikelets, and the toweling would not ruin its shape. Beneath the towel she wore, her body began to dry and warm, and as it did she felt a calmness return.

Next he asked, demanded, that she use the items he had laid out on the sink for her. Starting with the toothbrush and paste, she went through more than her ordinary morning ritual. Hovering as closely as a dentist, a beautician, a hairdresser, a masseur, a geisha, the sophomore busily supervised the way she shaved her legs, oiled and powdered her legs and shoulders, treated her complexion, plucked her eyebrows, applied her makeup, combed her hair, polished her nails, deodorized her underarms; but his interest was far from that of a detached professional's. It was instead the climaxing of a life-long passion gone childishly hysterical, like a serious art scholar's irresponsible giggle at seeing at last a real masterpiece in the flesh. At any moment she expected him to break into song, to clap his hands together and roll his eyes like Eddie Cantor. To be sure, there was still an undercurrent of violence, but on the surface the sophomore momentarily posed no more of a threat than one's kid brother stealing a look at things usually done behind closed doors. It wasn't until a week later that my wife experienced the awful sense of violation that was to haunt her the rest of her life. But there in the bathroom, with this Cheshire sophomore underfoot, she even considered the ridiculous idea that the only reason he had been able to make her undress and go to bed and wake up and shower and so on was because secretly she wanted to.

"Now let's get you dressed."

He led her out of the bathroom to the chest of drawers and found the one containing her underpants, a dozen pair in as many colors, all neatly folded in half, one on top of another in two identical piles of six each. He picked a shocking pink cotton pair, and held them out to her. Without removing the makeshift sarong, she slipped them on.

"I can't see them with the towel," he said, making a move toward the tuck that held it up. Instinctively she leaned back out of his reach and gauged the anger rising in his eyes. There was no shower to lose herself in, nowhere to turn and still keep an eye on him, nothing to do but stand there foolishly and awkwardly naked.

"I'll do it," she apologized.

She took it off with a trembling hand, held onto it; she felt a coolness against her breasts. Despite the sophomore's honesty, as he looked not at her breasts but at the shocking pink panties, she felt like a little girl who was wearing breasts the way a little boy wears his father's hat. She wished they would fall off. In her mind flashed the biological form of mankind, and it had no breasts. Only when a baby suckled one, or a man's hand caressed them, or a model posed them erotically did they make any sense. Hanging there on her scared little girl's body they were merely grotesque, impotent, humiliating symbols of utter inferiority. She would always hate him for that.

"Now these," he ordered, skipping over her breasts as he raised his glance from her panties to her eyes. He threw her a frilly white pair.

Even though he had not touched her, except that one time in the shower when he only spun her around, there was always the possibility that one wrong move, one refusal, one misinterpreted hesitation, anything that might cast doubt on his having the upper hand could turn this so far harmless pervert into a killer.

So she took off the shocking pink panties and pulled on the frilly white ones, a more revealing pair by far, nylon, tighter underneath so that they creased and bulged up the center and showed spots where her pubic hair was still wet from the shower. Still she clutched the towel, and also the pink panties.

"Now these." He tossed her a faded beige pair.

He made her put on all twelve till finally she stood in the last pair, plain blue cotton ones, the others scattered on the floor around her feet. When she had put on the fifth pair, she noticed that the fourth pair had left a stringy piece of lint dangling from her pubic hairs and she was too embarrassed to pick it off. It was still there during the next exchange, and the next, and the next one, too. But by then she had lost her embarrassment. Whether it was his intention or not, the sophomore was succeeding in dehumanizing her. All she really cared about after ten long minutes of swapping and modeling underpants was to escape being raped or beaten or killed, not whether a hair stuck unbecomingly out of the stained reinforcement in a polka-dot crotch.

"I like you in underpants," he said. "Every time I see a pretty girl, I picture her in underpants. That's how I picture her. That's how I always pictured you. And now here you are."

The sight of her seemed to hypnotize the sophomore. He widened his glassy gaze and spoke to his demons in a faraway voice.

But he snapped out of it just like that.

Riffling through the closet, pulling out pants and dresses and shirts and flinging them onto the floor, the sophomore finally stopped at a gray pantsuit.

"You were wearing this the first time I saw you."

My wife was never so happy to get dressed. She took the suit from the sophomore and had it on in seconds, including a white blouse that he handed her after she had slipped into the pants.

But a strange thing, a strange thing. Even after she was fully dressed, she felt as naked as before. And the sophomore sensed it, too. "Never again, never again," he kept repeating to himself as if it were a private joke. "Never again." Oh, that terrible, terrible smile of his, and the sinister way he kept shaking his head so that the entire upper part of his body rocked back and forth. A woman feels so helpless. She's so vulnerable. What if he lashed out at her or wanted to squeeze her to death or pin her to the wall or the floor and crush her with his hideous squirming weight?

And then the sophomore began to take off his own shirt. He

stood up and strolled casually about the tiny room, slowly unbuttoning the sleeves and the front and going on and on incoherently: "What's for dinner?" "Anything good on the tube tonight?" "Have a nice day, honey?" "I like that shade of lipstick." On and on, chanting almost, while she dared not move, on and on about weekend plans and the price of coffee and how close, how very close to a breakthrough in DNA, and just a sec, I have to pee, and the sophomore, who was bare-chested by this time, stopped circling her and went into the bathroom and urinated without closing the door so she could hear his noise, and then, in the sudden, shrill silence of the apartment, she heard him drive himself with whispered grunts and hushed, staccato, spoken hammer blows. It did not sound like ecstasy.

And then nothing. He came out of the bathroom with his tail between his legs, threw on his shirt, never once looked up at my wife, and left. Opened the door, went out, closed the door behind him, just left.

·

The television set began to flicker. The picture rolled down, disappeared, circled back up somehow, and then rolled down again.

I thought about calling the Hungarian and his friend. I wanted to see their reactions when they walked in through the kitchen and then when they crossed into the dining room and were faced with my wife's bloodless corpse and the stiffening children huddled within her last embrace. I wanted to watch their faces for any sign of guilt or torment or disgust or madness, believing at the same time that probably they would revert back to their earliest instincts and express any deep emotion or sudden shock in their native Hungarian, so that I would not be able to read the signs. They wouldn't do it on purpose, of course, but still what an effective mask, how brilliant and foolproof human nature could be.

The flickering was gathering speed. Soon my eyes could not keep the picture intact. I knew it was a man. Somehow I knew the man was nervous as he picked up where my mother had just left off. The voice belonged to Ray. Ray who was dead, Ray who was dying. Ray who was not home yet, Ray who was getting another treatment and losing another inch of his leg. It was the same voice as Ray's, a man's voice.

In the masculine resonance and nuance and tone were the secret masculine ingredients that go back to Adam and apes and the first barking fish; also a secret common knowledge that is chemical and anatomical and soaked up through the very process that forms the voice by chiseling away everything that is not the voice.

The voice in my head, in the TV set, in the wrinkled throat of my lame stepfather, rambled on with nervous excitement. It seemed to confess as well as condemn.

I wanted it to be more dramatic and to harvest the insidious possibilities already planted. Wouldn't it be incredible, I thought to myself, if the voice told me that the episode with the sophomore had so thoroughly debased my wife that she became the very incarnation of sinfulness, performing unimaginably lewd acts with anyone and everyone who happened onto our breezeway?

Then with a thumping, eerie background sound track of ukuleles, tom-toms, and synthesizers, with Five-O nosying around the door to my other life, the voice rose like a summer stream from the lush green hills of Hilo. There he was, the voice would explain, thousands of miles away, but wiring for the mainland papers every morning because he feared his wife was certain to become an embarrassment. There he was, lord of a compound of cottages by the sea, lord high trainer of lost souls who fled to the edge of the world for the salvation he promised. Weak, pitiful, troubled, men and women would beat down his door to bring him their last bit of savings while he stood above them in his unwrinkled white linen suit and chartreuse native shirt unbuttoned to the base of his suntanned sternum. Just be with me, he would tell them. Stay here with me for an hour, a day, a weekend, for as long as it takes. Listen to what I have to say, know that I love you and I can help you. And he and his tribe would walk the beaches and eat fresh pineapples, and every ten minutes he would stop and tell them they had found paradise and that their problems and despair were back home rotting in the cold of the Dakotas, in the slime of New York City, in the swampy Florida Everglades, in the smog, the fog, the desert sun, the sooty snow, along the oily Atlantic coast. The premise was simple: if they could experience paradise on earth, they would have paradise on earth. And then they could return to their squalid, depressing lives with a secret no amount of misfortune could destroy. And return they must, and promise to find and send another.

Alaya was his consort during the island sojourns. Each morning he picked an orchid and placed it in her silky black hair. Alaya was with him every moment. On the beach she would walk bare-breasted just behind the long, purposeful steps of the man in the unwrinkled white linen suit.

She was woman, he would say, putting his hand on her breast, and he was man. That was all. At dinner he drank from her shell and she from his. At midnight the tribe huddled outside the cottage of the lord and listened for the wisdom he could scream out during lovemaking. If, he taught, you could put it into words, if the power of a tidal wave of emotion and physical love could be transformed into language so that the mystery inherent in the squealing and sighing of passion were suddenly released, then wisdom can be made apparent. That was the secret of life, the word inside the moan. Never mind whether it made sense—wisdom never did—as long as it made poetry. And money.

And then at sunrise, Alaya still asleep in a bed of thick green fronds, he would wire the mainland for the news item he dreaded. Wife leads double life, wife turns home into brothel, wife found dead, violated, dismembered in a shantytown alleyway. So he had to put his dread to rest. With the success of his part-time other life in Hilo, he no longer could afford the reality or even the fantasy of the embarrassment his wife had come to symbolize. He had to arrange for her death.

Ten long years after her brush with the sophomore, two children later, after hundreds of business trips to Hilo during which he carefully, patiently, diligently drove his dream into the minds of paying customers, he called upon his next in command, Dano, Alaya's younger brother, the one man on earth to whom he entrusted his paradise on earth in his absence; he called upon Dano to preserve their kingdom by the sea, to kill his wife and children and make it look as though she had killed the children and then herself. That could easily be covered up. Such deaths would not interest the authorities.

How was he to know that while he stood in the surf sternly admonishing his followers to find more lost souls like themselves and bring them to where there was only happiness and wisdom and the poignancy of land and sea, that while he caressed Alaya's animal breast and bade the others to touch each other with the same direct love of man or of woman, that as he buttoned the middle button of his unwrinkled white linen suit and left unbuttoned the top three bottons of his chartreuse shirt, a pasty-faced, bespectacled lab assistant was dusting Dano's fingerprints on a Hilo Lounge matchbook?

But no, the voice I heard only spoke the sad, unvarnished, humdrum truth. The ukes and drums and stirring narration vanished. Instead I heard a ringing silence which finally, mercifully, broke into the tiny pieces of my ordinary tale.

I heard this tale from Ray as well as from myself. It was a man's story, and every man knew it and told it just as every woman had known the littlest detail in the story of my wife and her sophomore. As I remembered my mother sitting me down and painfully relaying what had happened to my wife while I was in Buffalo, and then swearing me to secrecy so that my wife would not be humiliated further by my mother's breach of confidence, I realized that I never once asked my mother how she came to know every panicky nuance, every gasp, every twisted turn of the plot. Of course she knew. What woman didn't?

From moderating or supervising so many focus group interviews, I had learned to read and trust the knowing shake of a head. I had found that there are some experiences everyone lives through regardless of whether that experience ever happened to him or her in fact. My mother felt she, too, was victimized by the sophomore and related to me what would have been, what probably were, her own reactions. And her own reactions were exactly like my wife's, certainly every bit as good in conveying the horror of the episode.

It would be nice if there were more to it than this, I thought, envisioning the family of corpses disentangled, cleaned up, and reposing peacefully, each in its own smooth coffin. More than an electronic hallucination. More than an unremarkable eulogy by someone who pretended to know the lives on exhibit.

But no. No, I never went to Hawaii and made animal love to Alaya and turned Dano into a hit man. Kojak wasn't interested in my case, nor was Ray a giddy, guilty informer doing Victor McLaglen for the sake of mankind's conscience.

I was doing it all.

Recognition is always a messy business. And I sat there slumped in front of flickering images, recognizing that yes, I had killed my wife and our children, but no court in the land would ever convict me. I could tell my story to a million souls, and they would only yawn or say that's an interesting philosophic viewpoint or else whisper behind my back that I was mad with grief, but not one of them would blame me. If they did, they would be destroying a world it took all of human history to build.

I got up and went to the garage. To get there I had to walk through the dining room, and I stepped in my wife's blood. From the kitchen I turned on the garage light, let myself out onto the breezeway, and opened the screened door that led outside to the backyard patio. A cool breeze caught my bare stomach, back, and thighs as I stood atop the little cement stairway that stepped down to the patio and led directly to the garage door.

Once inside the garage, I walked to a corner where my golf clubs leaned. I shouldered the heavy, damp, cobwebbed bag and struggled back across the floor, stepping in a nearly dry oil slick.

Hauling the clubs back into the den, I thought about how Ray had to keep altering his game as the surgeons kept altering his poisoned foot. I tried to make a joke out of it once, kidding him that he would have a great advantage whenever he faced an uphill lie or found the lip of a sand trap, but his handicap was growing week by week and the officials posted it on the fake wood paneling in the clubhouse, where the members inspected it as if it were Ray's medical chart and sighed under their breaths that they were glad it wasn't them.

I unzipped a pouch in the mildewed bag, found a dozen loose balls, and dropped them all at my feet.

Withdrawing the rusty shaft of my nine iron, removing the traces of dirt caught in the blade, I felt all the muscles in my body twinge involuntarily.

I never questioned my wife when it was obvious that she did not want me to know a thing about her near rape. But some things I did know. I knew that she had thrown away all of her underpants and bought ten new pair, although I pretended not to notice the charge when the bill came due. I knew that she did not want to make love for a long time afterwards and made excuses even when none were necessary, for I, too, had not been interested in performing beneath the phantom leer of the sophomore.

Unconsciously my hands formed a textbook grip about the frayed rubber handle of the club, my fingers tightening and loosening and retightening to make tiny adjustments.

To be honest, I had been disappointed that she felt she couldn't confide in me. But I would not have known what to do or say anyway. It had been a stroke of luck that I knew without her knowing that I knew. I had been able to comfort her merely by seeming naturally tolerant of her unusual and at times unreasonable behavior during the two or three months following the incident.

For example, she hadn't been able to say why, but she felt we ought to move as soon as possible. Knowing why, I agreed it was a good idea, instead of arguing the positive side of staying put until we had more money. To maintain my cover, probably more for my mother's sake than anyone's, I had made passes at my wife, but quickly turned them into foolishness or else dropped them altogether whenever she begged off. Sometimes I saved her the trouble of having to make an excuse by preempting her with "I think I'll go to sleep early tonight," or "I have a lot of work to do tonight." Other times I went out for a walk or a drink or a drive.

The slow, careful ascent of my backswing toppled a lamp from the Parsons table.

We found a new apartment in a different neighborhood, and, on the surface at least, my wife changed back to her old self the night we moved in. Halfway through dinner she started to eye me and nibble her hamburger suggestively.

That night she made noisy, sloppy love while I lay nearly passive in her fitful clutches.

The nine iron glanced off the ceiling and knocked me off balance. I swung wide and wild, flailing at the cluster of balls with the last remaining force of my deformed stroke.

And the next morning she awoke drained mentally and physically, a condition she never did snap out of.

A ball rocketed through the doorway, hit a picture in the hall, and caromed out of sight. Again and again I hacked at the balls, sending them in every direction. I could feel the sweat break out under my arms and in the small of my back. I hit my own foot with one mighty swing but repressed the pain while taking another five or six Ruthian swats. Each time the shaft flew down and made contact with the floor and a ball and the wall, I let out a whining grunt; the grunts became louder and alternated with sobs that together chorused the heaving of my body.

Finally one ferocious backswing landed the blade through the screen of the television, shorting out the picture and sound and sticking there inside the jagged glass hole. The immovable clubhead yanked me to the floor where I sat in a weeping, almost unconscious heap.

•

When I arrived home from work I found my wife had killed our two sons and taken her own life.

Almost at once I went into a daze. I must have had a drink or two. I think I searched the house for a killer. Like a zombie I took off all my clothes, threw them in a heap, and walked stupidly toward our backyard pool.

The swim temporarily shocked me out of my daze and into a chilly depression.

As I caught sight of myself in the moonlit water, Mrs. P., Mrs. P., Mrs. P., kept rippling through my mind. I wished she were in the cool water with me, the satiny Virginia Slims jacket gliding through the skim line like some animal from the moon, chlorinated droplets rolling off the silver smoothness, determined whirlpools inflating the jacket front as Mrs. P., Mrs. P., Mrs. P. spacewalked toward me in erotic slow motion.

She was altogether different from my wife. Physically, my wife was lean and delicate and without Mrs. P.'s unsophisticated gracefulness. Mrs. P. had that ease and self-confidence about her body that someone who works for a living unconsciously masters. She always knew what to do with her moving parts: flick a speck off the table with her fingers, hook a chair into place with her foot, search out the need that needed filling with her busy eyes. At the focus group interview Mrs. P. sat at the big conference table as though she lived there and felt it was up to her to keep the place comfortable and inviting. My wife, though I never actually spied her through a one-way mirror, would have sat stiffly and stared straight ahead at her notes or at the moderator. Physically and psychologically, the main difference between the two women was that Mrs. P. felt at home in the world, while my wife felt like a guest.

I went back inside the house. Too depressed and too disgusted to bother dressing, I fell into the chair facing the television, which someone had left playing.

There was Kojak. I imagined he was on my trail. I sat there rewriting my life and my wife's life so that the unheroic finality of my family's death did not overwhelm me. I'm sure that's why I didn't cry or scream. I spun mystery about myself to keep that awful, threatening *amen* from finishing off a rather undistinguished, and now completely irrelevant, twenty-five years.

God, did I know her that long?

Has it really been a quarter of a century, three quarters of my life, since we met in grade school and fell head over heels in lasting puppy love because she was cute and I was funny and because we giggled a lot and always seemed to have something else to say to one another the morning after a three-hour telephone conversation and because our mouths fit together nicely and she never minded my adolescent pimples and I never minded that she did not have big boobs?

Mrs. P. did have big boobs. They jiggled in her jacket when a response animated her

"Me, too," she jiggled. "I'd never use a tampon either," she agreed with Mrs. S., adding a shoulder shudder for emphasis.

It was to my wife's credit that no one ever made unkind cracks about her small breasts. Even in high school when a pointy sweater was the difference between staying home alone to watch "Gunsmoke" on Saturday night or being invited to make an entrance through the swinging doors of the rickytick saloon that profitably catered to our legal tastes of pizza and Coke, even then my wife's social life never suffered the same stunted fate as her figure. In fact, she was one of the most popular of all the girls, which no doubt drew me to her. And it had been a healthy popularity, too, not the result of French kissing or dry humping or backseat hand jobs or worse.

Of course, I couldn't be sure. But my hunch was that her being bright and funny and cute as a button was probably more than enough for even the most sex-starved teenage boys. What they discovered in my wife-to-be's company was that they were really only date-starved, companion-starved, starved for the tenderness boyhood adolescence brashly disdained, and as far as sex was concerned, they were all too willing to fast again another day, still bloated from feasting alone the night before.

Our own relationship was another matter, full of strategies and counterstrategies, despite both our convictions that sooner or later we'd wind up together. Reduced to its simplest formula, she did love me but wanted to be sure; I did love her and decided why bother loving anyone else. That is why, through the first few years of college, she dated every kind of boy—athlete, scholar, actor, marketing major, premed, Negro, motorcyclist, rich, poor, handsome, dumpy, so long as he had a pecker—and why my entire social life was just another mark on her calendar.

I realized that I was mad at my wife. I didn't mean to think that she had actually had sexual relations with all her dates, just the opposite, dog honest. But why did she have to lead me on, make me jealous, condemn me to watch "Gunsmoke" when I could hardly concentrate, when what was happening on Make-Out Lane or in Weequahic Park, or at Asbury Park, or in the whorehouse-dark aisles of the Park or Roosevelt or Hawthorne or Maple theaters was far more threatening than the gun barrel staring Matt Dillon and me in the face?

She did have sex with me; that was my trump card. Let the others keep her in malteds and movies; when she was out with me . . .

At some point my mother called and I kept quiet about the bodies; I handled my end of the conversation coolly so as not to arouse any suspicions.

My mother was in my thoughts. So was Ray, my stepfather. I seemed to be running from him, running toward my mother. Like those good old teenage boys, I yearned for the tenderness no man would dare show me.

How tender was our lovemaking. It was never stilted, never clumsy, even when it was. That came from our having been two months to the day short of the exact same age, having grown up in the same social climate, and having shared identical apprehensions. When I blamed myself for failing to slip it in like an old pro, she blamed herself for not knowing it was up to her to help guide me. Only later on, after her experience with the sophomore, did our love life start coming apart.

I wondered, if that had happened to Mrs. P., whether or not it would have affected her behavior in bed. Mrs. P. probably would have felt honored, "chosen," possibly even sexually aroused by the blond bandit. Well, wasn't he a bandit, hadn't he stolen sacred human privacies from my wife? In one insanely daring chess move he had mated her, putting her naked back to the wall, literally mated her without having to pay the price of sex, marriage, and family . . . or the finance charges.

To me that was what sex was all about. A door to be opened that revealed your partner in all her gloriously private moments. It was never bare breasts or a wet clitoris or a wriggling ass that a woman wanted to keep from you. It was the privacy that had to be revealed along with her naked sexuality: the way she slept, snored, dressed, showered, ate, read, listened, moved, spoke, thought. And that sneaking sophomore, acting out every man's deepest fantasy, had gotten through that door, talked his way in, glimpsed the truly sacred stuff, and, as a result, left my wife as violated as a bleeding Sabine woman. All her private mannerisms, all the things that were mine alone, and made her mine, now belonged to him, too. That is the real meaning of giving it away. That is the real meaning of being deflowered. No more fancy, frilly, lacy petals to veil the mystery.

But why hadn't she come to me? Why did she go to my mother, not even her own? It was almost as if she knew her mother was going to be the first to die, and didn't want her to take the secret with her to the grave. Or perhaps she was counting on my mother to tell me after all. I was like my mother. If my wife had told me a secret, I would have found a way to spill it. I never could bear secrets. And sure enough, the first thing my mother had done was blab it to me.

"Kojak" ended and "Hawaii Five-O" came onto the screen. A beautiful native girl double-crossed a maniacal killer, and everyone knew he would get her. She needed more than police protection. She was paranoid, and Dano, the chief of Five-O's right-hand man, said he hoped the girl didn't kill herself just to be rid of the fear of being killed.

It was comforting to recall our early days together. In all our hot and eager innocence, the gritty pavement of the city sidewalks felt like sand beneath our feet. A cramped, steering-wheel-hampered embrace in my mother's lumbering Pontiac had seemed as spiritually unencumbered as Burt Lancaster and Deborah Kerr's eternal embrace in the Hawaiian surf. But I never begged her to date only me. That was my strategy. She'd see my worth more clearly in comparison. And she never asked me to date others. That was her strategy. She didn't want to risk losing the bird in the hand that twittered and puffed itself up as she stroked it. Mostly we avoided the subject. As long as neither one of us pressed the issue of her social promiscuity or my long-suffering loyalty, we could go on and on. For all our hysterical teenage acrobatics, there was still a net below.

Also we were both made old beyond our years by the artistic environment at school. Our closest friends were a new literati hatched by the egghead rebellion that came to be known as the beat generation.

These friends formed their own high school literary magazine and only surprised me by not calling it something as obvious as *Despair* or *Dirge* or even *Death* itself. Between the graveyard howlings of cafe poets, the fuck-the-phonies attitude of Holden Caulfield, the brutal satire of literary comedians like Lenny Bruce and Mort Sahl, the city-wise folksiness of offbeat pickers like the Kingston Trio, and the gloomy pronouncements in *Hari Kari*, the clever name finally given to the literary magazine, my wife and I could hardly suppress our existential nausea. Even if we hadn't actually experienced it, we were made to feel the hopelessness and futility of life's big con twenty years before the natural course of our American lives would have automatically shown us the nothingness of it all. What Jack and J. D. and Miles and Ingmar and Jean-Paul and Albert and all the rest had done was rob us of twenty blissfully ignorant years. Our premature sense of nihilism, dread, death, and the void that awaited were as solid as the geometry Mr. Moscowitz tried to teach us. But Mr. Moscowitz never appeared in a black turtleneck and furrowed brow. He tried to tell us about the good, rich, mathematically proven past, but how could he compete with the impassioned ranting and raving of the new voice that rasped through a black hole in the tortured face of one who had just seen the future? And if the future was even half as bleak as the voice predicted, why not accept the tender, joyous love you were lucky enough to have already found? Even my wife who, like her mother, was cautious about any commitment, shortened by seven years the ten years of experimental oat-sowing her inherited common sense recommended. Me, I was doomed from the very start, from the death of my father, from the sight of my mother pleading for her casketed Snookums to wake up, I was doomed to take life as it came, to love one hunk of beating animal matter as well as another, since both were destined for the scrap heap. The games you had to play, the wiliness one had to summon up just to coax batting lashes from a date—it all seemed such a waste of time and energy.

What did it all matter?

I had always assumed I was right and life had always borne me out. My dead father in his funny funeral-home makeup, my wife's dead mother, the three dead bodies on the dining room carpet, the five of them, plus countless other disappointments, miseries, torments, nightmares, and assorted carbuncles of the soul had vindicated my motto, my slogan, my weary battle cry.

The worst night of them all, worse than the sicknesses and death prayers, was not even worth dredging up again. Better not to know if that sailor was lying. Better not to care. Anyway, now it was too late to ask my wife the truth, dog honest. On the other hand, now I could ask her without worrying about the answer, dog honest.

I wondered if I would ever say that again: dog honest, our little code expression under which my wife and I felt bound to tell the absolute truth. Strangely enough, having devised our private vow to get at the truth, more often it was purposely *not* used to keep the truth hidden. I never asked my wife to tell me, dog honest, what had happened between her and that sailor because I really did not want to know, or because I did not want to force her into telling me something that would make both of us unhappy. Nor did I question her, dog honest, about the true cause of her strange behavior following the episode with the sophomore. And never did I sense this purposeful avoidance of the magic phrase more than when my wife seemed to want to know where I was and what I was doing throughout most of the nights of her first pregnancy. She wanted to know, she believed she did know, but she certainly didn't want me to confirm her worst suspicions, dog honest.

Our cat leaped into my naked lap and walked in two little circles before convincing herself that I offered no comfortable spot.

Of course, now there was nothing to stop me from assigning my own truth to her date with the sailor: a simple, classic, nasty knee to his balls. Oh, yes. It gave me a great, gloating pleasure to picture that handsome tar doubled over, throwing up, a look of virginal disbelief on his smug Hollywood face.

It was a college orientation weekend at a dismal camp. Entering freshmen could spend two days in the country getting to know each other and asking the teacher-counselors any gnawing questions about collegiate life.

My wife-to-be and I decided to go. But we had different motives. I thought it was a great opportunity to be alone with her for two days. She thought it was a wonderful way to meet and size up college men.

From the moment we climbed out of the chartered bus, I sensed that this was going to be another of my horribly traumatic camp experiences. Twice my parents had bused me off into the great outdoors, once having to come and rescue a feverish, malnutritioned, and poison-ivied seven-year-old, and the second time having to send the police out to search for a runaway.

But college orientation was to be a different kind of anguish. In retrospect, it was to be the ultimate test of my loyalty and my wife's curiosity.

We lived in cabins. In mine there were three other freshmen: one obviously political-minded fellow who wanted a head start on capturing votes for president of the freshman class; one underweight refugee from a parochial school who prayed all the first night for an early sunrise so we could choose up sides for softball that much sooner; and then there was the sailor.

He had even packed his things in a weathered duffel bag and slung it around in the theatrical manner of an older, more experienced, bejees, a dog-honest seafarin' gob of a show-off.

His main purpose at camp and in life was to get laid. He regaled the three of us with stories of his worldwide conquests and promised us there wasn't a piece of ass that could refuse him from here to Timbuctoo.

As he unpacked he rambled on about fucking as though it were both the most fundamentally sublime and the most degrading experience on earth. There was nothing quite like that explosive crash of contact, he assured us, between dick and Jane, and nothing worse, he warned, than waking up in your own puke because it took a fifth to get her into fourth. And after every anecdote, he gave us a knowing wink and said, "But I don't have to tell you guys what I'm talking about, do I?" He honestly believed that we three sexual landlubbers were all in the same boat.

He was so busy, he fussed with the sheet corners of his bunk and the organization of his locker as if there were going to be an inspection. Carefully he smoothed away any wrinkles from the outfit he was going to wear that night. He brushed his short hair and flashed his blue eyes and adjusted the white collar of his frayed, fashionably inappropriate dress shirt.

Our first night at camp he made it perfectly clear whose ass he was after. There was a tone of sharp steel in his voice that said "hands off" when he talked about my wife. And with his slight but well-muscled physique, the sailor looked like he could easily hold his own if it came to a showdown.

It would have been bad enough, I remembered without wanting to, if the sailor had idly decided to make a play for my wife. But apparently the two of them had already talked to one another and planned to meet down at the lake's edge at midnight. When I first found the cabin, only the softballer was inside; the sailor didn't arrive for another twenty minutes. So it was possible that he had met and plotted with my wife. It was possible. My wife-to-be.

I lay there in a furiously hot and directionless agony while the sailor undressed and did a salty jig in anticipation of the midnight crash between trusty dick and newfound Jane. My Jane.

Why did he have to pat himself on his bulge and sprinkle talc inside his underpants?

Finally, when I couldn't stand watching him a second longer, when I thought I was about to throw up all my vital organs, I ran out of the cabin and found the slightly less ramshackle quarters where the girls were primping. I skulked around back to a small window and looked in. Although I'd be seeing her in a little while at dinner, I had to talk to my wife immediately. I tapped against the window until a short, fat girl with a cluster of pimples for a nose noticed. "The girl with the ponytail," I mouthed and pointed. At last my wife saw me and came to the window.

"I have to talk to you," I said, trying to suppress the desperation I was feeling.

But she motioned that she couldn't understand me through the closed window. She shrugged her shoulders and made an apologetic face and finally gave up. "I'll see you at dinner," she said as I read her lips.

I still can't figure out why neither of us had dared open the window or what had kept us from meeting outside the door to her cabin. Perhaps we thought college had already begun and we had better be on our best behavior.

At dinner we sat next to each other, which didn't seem to bother my wife or the sailor. I comforted myself with the thought that maybe he had piped us aboard a barely floating ship, maybe he hadn't consulted my wife after all about his midnight plan.

As was my customary strategy, I acted relaxed and only half-expectant when I suggested through invisibly chattering teeth that my wife-to-be sneak out after curfew and meet me somewhere. How did down by the lake sound?

She didn't say no, but she didn't say yes, either. She wanted to play it by ear, see how the night went, why did we have to lock ourselves into something now, we could see one another anytime, why not try to meet some of the other kids?

Nothing I could remember was as painful as that night. Not tonight, not even the eerily invisible vapor of doom that hung in the hallway between my dark end of the tunnel and the tangle of bodies barricading the other end could compare with the dense gloom that weighed on me throughout our cold camp dinner of ham and Swiss, potato chips, slice of pickle, container of milk.

She had actually given me the brush and smiled and sounded reasonable all through it. She was actually going to rendezvous with him at the edge of the lake while everyone else, myself included, was supposedly sleeping tight, not letting the bedbugs bite, red eyes at night, sailor's delight, black eye in the morning, sailor take warning.

I laughed. I heard the laugh pop out by itself. Dog honest was at last burying the bones of that long ago night when I came as close as any man ever did to castrating himself.

"It sounds to me like you've already lined something up for yourself," I teased, sneaking in the same half-serious accusation, or a variation on its theme, every time the freshman who thought she was Joan Baez paused between her whining, guitar-strangling dirges that turned out to be the evening's only entertainment.

"We've never had a chance like this to be alone," I romanced as the teacher-counselor continued his remarks by saying, "Remember, you're not alone. Everyone here and everyone in the entire freshman class is in the same boat. With the competitiveness out there and the demand for college graduates, it's a real sink-or-swim situation. If you make the grade, it's clear sailing for life. If you don't, you're going to miss the boat."

"Don't you love me?" I groveled, as the curfew whistle blew and my wife-to-be obediently headed for her cabin.

"Maybe I'll stop by later and throw a pebble at your window," I called after her, thinking that might unnerve her. But the thought of peeking in the window and catching her sprinkling talc inside those baby blue, baby-soft underpants I was sure she had taken along unnerved *me* instead.

An hour and forty-five minutes to go, I kept dreading as I shuffled across the compound, past the Dogpatch outhouse, over the little footbridge that spanned the dried-out creek separating the boys' cabins from the girls', and along the unkempt hedgerow that wound to the front door of my shack. However rundown and neglected the campsite was, it seemed even worse at that moment. The three-quarter darkness shrouded the grounds, the shrubs, the lopsided little shacks, and the shadow campers splitting out of shadow quartets and wobbling their separate ways home. The overall mood was as gray and grim as Dachau. My overall mood, I guess.

Inside, I flopped down onto my bunk with all my clothes on and lit a cigarette. I shut my eyes and concentrated on the color blue. Light blue. Baby blue. I pictured pools and clouds and the cover of a poetry book I had, and then I realized that except for the sky and the police and some sunny, faraway oceans, blue was not one of society's predominant colors. It didn't mean stop or go or wait or beware or exit or entrance. Roses had to be dyed blue, and, besides blueberries, you never ate blue food, for fear it had gone bad. There was, in fact, something intangible or unreal about blue. Like Superman's hair. Or Billie Holiday's songs. Or the best stocks. Or the rarity of a certain kind of moon. Or pornographic movies. Or a worker's collar. Or outer space. Powder blue was a color everyone had some idea of, yet I couldn't remember ever seeing a blue powder, and I had seen most of them during my part-time high school career as a clerk in a drugstore. Blue flames were common enough, but the red and orange ones were so much bolder you really had to stare and concentrate to catch sight of one of those timid, quick-flickering blue ones. Blue was, I decided, an intellectual color, an emotional idea, an apt description of the sadness and loneliness that visited in the night. It was a good color for songs. "Am I blue, you'd be, too." A paradoxically cheerful color that somehow seemed to go with the saddest, most desperate feelings. Over and over again, no matter how hard I tried to push it out of my mind, blue was the color of my wife-to-be's precious, private underpants.

"Got a date with an angel, gonna meet her at midnight . . ."

The sailor literally blew in through the door like a sea storm lashing open a hatch. Nothing could keep him away from me.

". . . and I'm on my way to the lakeside."

He whirled and jumped and tap-danced around the cabin singing the corrupted lyrics of his wild song with the same crazy energy Sammy Davis Jr. had wrung out of himself when my wife and I saw him at the Copa on our prom night. He was little, too, like Sammy, and I imagined that his talc'd and patted dick was every inch as enormous as the popular black myth promised even little Sammy Davis Jr.'s was.

Every time the sailor got to a certain phrase in his song, he whacked the future president of the freshman class on his stomach for rhythmic emphasis. Not wanting to alienate a single voter, the unofficial candidate smiled as big and as hard as if he, too, were going to drive one of those big black bat handles through the faintly damp vee of my baby's baby-blues.

"Da da da da da da-da, da da da da da da-da. . . . Hey, who you guys got lined up for later, huh? You see the torpedos on that chick who was playin' the guitar? I thought she was gonna get 'em all caught up in her strings or something. I'll tell you, big tits are great and all that, but you don't fuck tits, you know what I mean? Oh, yeah, maybe in Paris they get a thrill out of tit-fuckin', you know, stickin' it imbetween a big pair and squishin' 'em together so it's kind of like the real thing, but shit, man, that's like a practice drill. That ain't fuckin'."

He seemed to know so much about the subject. I had never even heard of tit-fucking, let alone been experienced enough to form an opinion about it.

"So who you got, matey?" he asked me.

I told him I had a migraine headache, and was sorry as soon as I heard myself saying it. What kind of an excuse was that for a man? And sure enough the sailor prescribed "two ass pins and don't bother callin' her in the morning."

It was an eternity until the sailor finally finished getting himself ready for my wife. An hour and a half of singing, brushing his hair, buttoning all the buttons on his sailor suit, spit-shining his shoes till I hoped they might glow in the dark and get him caught before he was fifty yards from the cabin. And, of course, there were more stories about his conquests when he was on leave in Australia and on leave in San Francisco and loving 'em and leaving 'em at all his other ports of call.

Finally, mercifully, his bezeled chunk of a watch reported that it was approaching 2400 hours.

"See ya, mateys," he crowed. "Next time ya lay eyes on me, I'll be a virgin no more," he giggled.

I was up on my feet before the sound of the door slamming shut behind him stopped reverberating. How could anyone be that self-confident? He didn't even steal out the door, as I was planning; he just threw it open, danced out, and slammed it shut. What simple-minded self-confidence, I comforted myself. I wondered if the navy had taught him that. Just walk right up to the enemy and bop him on the head.

It was now pitch-black outside. Except for the skyline, everything looked like a haystack or a tepee or a giant bundle of firewood, shapeless, unyielding, unlike whatever it really was. Only the very tops of trees or cabins or water towers against the slightly lighter sky made any visual sense. The first step I took landed me in the hedges, and the prickly branches scratched my bare legs. I had to sort of slide my feet along the ground and feel with my outstretched hands until my eyes grew accustomed to the darkness.

I didn't mind how slowly I had to make my way, because it gave me time to try and figure out what I was doing. I knew I wanted to go to the edge of the lake, but I didn't know what I might do when I got there. Was I going to yell "Aha!" and spring out of the bushes like a character out of Dickens? Was I going to spy silently on the two of them, stifling tears and hatred and delaying a confrontation until a less emotional occasion arose? It even crossed my mind that I might walk steadily toward the shore and into the murky lake until the still, dark waters swallowed me whole.

How had I allowed myself to become so jealous? It was a revelation to me. My love was not as matter-of-fact as I had thought. Maybe I loved her as well as love another, but I had underestimated the intensity of my feelings. A low-hanging branch knocked the sense of it all into me. It didn't graze me, it smacked flush into my forehead and produced an almost instantaneous lump. As I sat cross-legged in the dirt, letting tears roll down my cheeks and pressing one hand against my throbbing forehead, I realized that life and love did make a difference to me. That I would rather be alive. Rather love her. The direction I had taken had been neither accidental nor incidental; I was actually in love with a very specific girl, and she was about to insult that love, bury it at sea, and it was up to me to rescue it or drown trying.

My pace quickened, even though my headache and teary eyes somehow blackened the already impenetrable night. I had no idea if I was heading for the kitchen, the largest structure in the compound and the only landmark along the way to the lake. But I kept going, faster and faster, until I came to what had to be the kitchen. An even blacker blackness loomed in front of me, which I took to be the long, crude barracks where a few hours earlier we had all dined together and I had not yet been fully convinced that my wife would throw away an unchaperoned night on a stranger.

I groped my way along the outside of the kitchen like a prisoner at the big wall that stood between him and freedom. Twice I felt splinters stab my palms. I kept sniffing, trying to get a whiff of proof that indeed I had found the kitchen.

Finally the building ended and I was beyond it. The ground began to slope radically. I knew I was heading down the hillside and that the lake was at the bottom. Thank God for all those buttons, I remembered thinking at the time; according to my calculations it would be one in the morning by the time the lakeside lovers would be through with small talk and halfway through with the sailor's suit.

Never having been down to the lake, I had no real way of knowing if I was on the right track. It seemed impossible that two lovers, starting from different points, could ever hope to find each other in this brambled, aimless pudding of night.

Unless they met at her cabin. Or out in back of my own.

A shiver of panic telescoped through my body as I imagined my wife and my sailor never having left the vicinity of my cabin. The talk about the lake's edge was all a ploy to throw me off his track; or the two midnight revelers, realizing that the night was darker than they had anticipated, decided to stick close to home instead; or when they met they were so attracted to each other that they didn't want to waste one precious moment getting into his white bells and her baby-blues.

While all this went spinning through my head, my pace picked up too much speed. Suddenly I realized I was running, and the downgrade was increasing with every longer and longer leap. I had visions of myself snowballing down the hill, growing in mass and speed, picking up loose branches and leaves and sleepy wood animals with the magnetic, breakneck, plowing plunge of my runaway descent. The black, shapeless shadows of the hillside whizzed past me. Twenty yards ahead, I could barely make out the trunk of a tree. I glanced up and saw the topmost limbs form an eerie maze against the sky. From the size of the biggest limbs I calculated that the trunk was small enough to be encircled by my arms, and I took a deep breath, believing that if I failed to brake myself by grabbing hold of the tree, I would race—fall—tumble—roll to a certain, muddy death in the scary deep, perhaps even lose an arm or my head along the way.

All the air rushed out of my body as I slammed into the tree. My momentum carried me farther, and I swung around the trunk, the jagged bark ripping at the flesh of my arms and legs. I had to let go, but the crash had broken my speed and I fell to rest on the ground, bleeding, breathless, barely conscious. A thousand bolts of pain crisscrossed, zigged, zagged, penetrated, scraped along the surface of my body. Then I was numb. I lay there for a few moments with only my head functioning, feeling as though I were buried from the neck down in a gooey anthill, less and less aware of the sharp little nibbles the man-eating ants were taking from my torn and bloodied flesh. And then all the pain seemed to focus itself between my legs. It wasn't a stinging, pulsing pain. It wasn't a dull ache. The pain felt like tentacles slowly swirling around in the cloudy underwater at the bottom of my stomach. It was a writhing, churning, slow-motion pain that doubled and tripled and quadrupled back upon itself, sprouting new tentacles, swaying anew in the conjugating clouds of murky composition. Sand and water. Nausea. Writhing, slimy tentacles. Amoeboid suckers gluing themselves to the wobbly walls of my stomach. Just to remember them tended to re-create the world of that pain all over again, as I sat numbly and dumbly in front of the flickering TV.

I sat there remembering how I had lain there. It would have been useless to try to get up.

I was afraid to reach into the central pain to see what I had done to myself. What if I had ripped my private parts clear out of their sockets? What if the whole works was just dangling by a little thread of flesh? The pain was so general, so obscure, that anything might have happened. Paranoiacally sure that I had castrated myself, I begged for sleep. Unable to get up, unable to administer the surgery I imagined I needed, all that was left was sleep. Surprisingly, it took almost no effort to push myself over the little ridge of consciousness that stood between my pain and the release from pain that sleep provided.

By morning I was stiff and scabby. The old pain was gone, and in its place was just a vague soreness. I looked around and saw that I was nowhere near the lake. If I had gotten to the kitchen at all, I had taken off from it in an opposite direction than I had thought, following the hillside down its southern slope toward the dirt road our chartered bus had coughed along yesterday afternoon. The lake was probably directly behind me, at the foot of the other side of the hill.

When I stood up, I could see the scabs all over my legs and arms. I had to disconnect some of the underbrush from clotted scrapes. Timidly I felt myself between my legs, and the gentle probing assured me that I had not come undone. But there was a sharp pang where my dick was.

I unbuttoned my shorts, unzipped them, pulled down my underpants, and gingerly extended the shaft for a closer examination. There was a thin lightning bolt of blood the length of my dick that culminated in a large ragged tear just beneath the brim of what had always looked like a fireman's hat to me. I had very nearly torn the head right off. But it was not as bad as it looked. The worst pain had been from unsticking my underpants from the gelatinous streak of clotted blood. As I carefully tucked myself back into my pants, I pictured Sammy Davis Jr.'s eely third dancing leg being jammed back into his sailor pants, its involuntary twitching sending up little smoke signals of talcum powder.

What happened, I wondered, as I limped back up the hill. I was still wondering what had happened almost twenty years later.

I went directly to the infirmary. Dr. Fisher was in charge, a robust, barrel-chested GP who also taught two classes in anatomy at the undergraduate level. While he patched me up, I noticed that someone was sleeping rather restlessly on one of the cots behind a gauzy curtain.

"Who's that?" I asked the doctor, trying to change the subject from what had happened to me. I had told him the truth, only I made it happen at 10:15 instead of at midnight, and that seemed to satisfy him. Mostly he was preoccupied with keeping me from flinching each time he daubed one of my abrasions with alcohol; but he kept musing aloud that it just hadn't seemed all that dark out to him last night at curfew time.

"Bees," he said matter-of-factly.

The figure behind the curtain struggled up to a sitting position, and her mammoth breasts immediately identified her as the torpedo girl the sailor had tried to sell us the night before.

"She walked into a hive, poor thing. Must have a hundred stings all over her. Got a call in to the local hospital now. Even got her on the soles of her feet, can you imagine that?"

Actually, what I was already imagining was the story I could tell the sailor and my wife about the wreck of my body. In the light of day, now that whatever had happened between them was over, I was more interested in preserving my dignity than in challenging theirs.

The walk back to my cabin took me across the ball field where, in answer to my skinny bunkmate's prayers, a softball game was already in progress. As I limped through the outfield, I looked for the sailor, but he was neither fielding, at bat, nor waiting in the on deck circle. Skinny was pitching, and the next president was catching, so I didn't have to worry about explaining my condition or last night's whereabouts just yet.

When I slammed the cabin door behind me, it woke up the sailor who had been sleeping, fully clothed, in my bunk. He opened his eyes, closed them again, and begged me to be quiet. On the floor, next to his dangling arm, was an empty pint bottle of vodka.

"You're in my bed."

"Hey, matey, can't you give a guy a break? Can't you see I'm hurtin', matey?"

"What about me? Look at me."

"What about you? I'm fuckin' dyin'. I got no brains left. I got no stomach left. Man, what a time we had," he said unconvincingly.

He raised himself up onto one elbow. His crewcut was impossibly disheveled.

"I'm tellin' ya, matey, I ain't got a thing left."

Had he gotten my wife drunk? She almost never drank. Did she take a few swallows and turn into the kind of sexual banshee that could have drained the life out of trusty dick?

"Yeah, well, old torpedo-tits really did a number on me, too," I heard myself brag.

One sailor eye opened and looked me up and down.

"Remember what she was doing to that guitar? Well, she did the same thing to me. We even fucked up a beehive. Stung my dick to hell and back."

If the sailor and my wife had truly spent the night in drunken ecstasy, surely, I figured, they would spend the rest of the weekend reliving it . . . or trying to revive it. And in their conversations, surely the sailor would have to bring up the subject of how torpedo-tits had strummed and picked and sicced bees on one of his mates. Of course that wouldn't be the story I'd give to my wife. I'd tell her the same half-truth I told Dr. Fisher and wait for her to put two and two together. I congratulated myself on the tension I had just created, the taut skin I had stretched between the three of us. Who would wrinkle up the three-way relationship first?

For twenty years all the questions had just floated under that skin. I could never be sure whether or not my wife had allowed herself to be liquored up and fucked senseless by the hung-over sailor. But if she had, then for twenty years she too lived—and died—with a great doubt: did I really plunge through the black forest that night, or did busty, bees-ey Baez wring every last drop of music from my poor battered instrument?

Like so many other things that had happened to us, we avoided ever talking about camp weekend. I slept Saturday afternoon, had dinner brought to me by the next president, slept some more Saturday night, and was hobbling about the kitchen Sunday morning like a soldier who had just been sent home after taking a pound of shrapnel along with Dirt Road Hill. By the time breakfast was over, my wife was chummy again, although she didn't volunteer how she had spent Friday and Saturday nights. For twenty years we simply pretended that the weekend never happened. We never joked about it, never felt a sudden compulsion to tell the truth, never even dared to mention it aloud.

It had made a difference, though. She no longer acted one-hundred-percent sure of me. She dated others the first years of college, not the sailor so far as I knew, but they were always one-time dates that took her to public places like Broadway or the opera or a rock concert or to a school dance.

It all passed neatly away. I didn't even carry any scars. And now I could know for sure that it had all been innocent, dog honest. The sailor had tried, my wife had turned him down. He emptied his pint himself and got rough with her. So rough she had to kick him where it counts. There are some things, I thought, that we have to believe just to preserve our sanity. That kick was one of them.

For whatever reason, she lost a good deal of confidence. Our relationship gradually shifted so that all the power flowed to my side. In our sophomore year she was already uninterested in her studies, preferring to steal time from classes and homework to take part in a vaudeville production that was to be the school's first variety show.

Oh, how she wanted to be an actress. In high school she had joined the drama club, but three times they gave her small and silly parts that suited her childish looks and little voice. Still the dream persisted, even overshadowing the fascination the biology lab held for her. That was her second love. Naturally it was the first to go, because with a little hard work it might have been attainable. Playing one of those meaty Tennessee Williams's women was not attainable. So naturally she ached for it with every bone in her and Laura Wingfield's body.

Somehow she managed to graduate and even win a postgraduate fellowship. But we were married the weekend after graduation ceremonies, and that was the end of school. Immediately she began playing the role of wife to the hilt. As a token gesture to the doctorate she knew she'd never try to earn, she took a secretarial job in the biology department, which gave her parents false hope that she was not really going to throw away so promising a career, that someday soon she would go back and make them proud.

The blue Hawaiian sky reminded me of our honeymoon in the Caribbean. We splurged on a week at a sprawling hotel. It was the first extended time we had ever had alone together. All alone. All night alone. Not counting college orientation camp.

It was warm and sunny and I ached to play golf. Dutifully she suggested we go out as a twosome and that I teach her the basics. I was not a low scorer, but I had a natural swing that sent the ball a country mile; too often, however, the ball landed in the wrong country. But I loved the game nonetheless. Truly golf was a game of mastery—over the wind, the sun, the water, the sand, the trees, the hills, the long grass, the slick grass, the rocks, the day in general, life in general, the universe. Whenever I played, the world seemed to roll out away from me on all sides and meet with infinity. Every distance looked insurmountable, and then, thwack, the little ball soared past brown and green, up through blue and blazing yellow, till it spanned time itself, till it bridged my place and some future place which no one had ever explored.

But as far away from the here and now as it took me, it was a fiercely internal game as well. Each stroke had to be measured against my own best ability. Each lie marked my skill. Each looping course of the ball was an extension of something inside my arms and legs that resembled a tracer, a fiery trail of muscle and coordination and concentration. How often one sees a golfer who has just finished his swing stand stone-still, arms still up, eyes intently following the ball till it rolls to a halt; he never moves, even if he loses it in the sun, he is part of the ball's force, his whole body points after it as if any little move he makes will throw the ball off target and into a trap. Even when part of a twosome, threesome, foursome, one is essentially alone, playing not against partners or opponents, but against the perfect grip, the perfect swing, the true arc, the invisible track in the grass that leads to the cup, against the coming together of all parts of the game for one complete hole and then another and another, and then one complete round.

But she had no talent whatsoever for it. The shortest iron was like a telephone pole in her hands.

"Watch me. Watch how I do it. Look at my left arm, it never bends."

The bag was too burdensome, the heat too stifling. After four holes she was content to drag along with me until the ninth green, which was spread just in front of the clubhouse.

"Are you sure you don't mind if I wait for you at the clubhouse?" she asked, as we trudged toward my second shot on the long, rolling dogleg par five ninth.

"I hate to leave you all by yourself," she said, as I withdrew my untrusty four wood and sighted the flag waving three hundred light-years away.

I stood over the ball for a small eternity, tensing every muscle, wriggling my feet slightly, squeezing the grip, making miniscule adjustments only I could barely feel.

"I could get a thermos of iced coffee . . ."

My arms flew back, my neck forcing my head down.

". . . if you'll wait . . ."

Slowly I began to uncoil, whipping power into my arms and wrists and club from deep inside my back and shoulders and thighs.

". . . and then I'll walk along with you."

I knew I should not have been able to hear her, but I did; the armor of concentration was incomplete, the tiny adjustments were coming undone as I threw myself into forward motion. The clubhead was a fraction too high as it exploded into the ball and sent it off toward the flag. No height. No loft. The ball zoomed ahead barely a foot off the ground. And then suddenly it stopped.

I ran to the spot like a wild man, my wife calling after me in a panicky, puzzled voice.

"What's the matter?! What happened?!"

She ran after me and grabbed hold of me when she got there to keep from collapsing with exhaustion.

"It must have run into it," I said.

She turned her face into my chest so she wouldn't have to look. But I could not take my eyes off the shattered head, the empty eye, the blood-trickling muzzle of the reddish brown rabbit.

Five, six, seven times I swung a driver crazily until I drove myself to the floor of the den. One of those swings broke the television screen. Another one broke my toe.

The pain in my toe was unbearable. It made me howl and cry tears.

Why did she do it? Why? Could I have known that this was what she was planning? All those quiet years in front of the television, should I have seen a clue? Were the names of all those inane television programs part of an anagram or cryptogram that spelled murder and suicide?

Between the bourbon, the wild golf swings, the loss of strength from being naked, and the shock (there must have been a shock), I felt myself begin to drift off into unconsciousness. It seemed as if the den were swarming with bees. Outside, the night noises were loud and clear. Two birds chattering. Highway traffic. The clothesline leash wheeling back and forth. A boat whistle.

It was not that late. If she were alive, she would be looking for a good movie on television. She loved television. Too much. She was consumed by it. I was glad I had smashed it in. I was vaguely aware of our cat sniffing the shattered screen. Her life was canned like the laughter or mood music on the soundtracks. Glad I smashed it in. Glad I . . .

•

The awful whine of a siren woke me up. It might have been Kojak. It might have been Five-O. In my half-asleep head the jig was up.

I got to my feet and stumbled through the hallway. When I saw the dead bodies on the dining room floor, I suddenly felt the terrible pain in my toe.

I lurched past my family, holding onto walls and cabinets and the refrigerator and the kitchen table until I was able to get to the back door. As I let myself out onto the breezeway, I realized it was very early morning. There was still mist in the street. A spinning red light was churning the mist.

"What the hell's going on?" I demanded, steadying myself on a drainpipe, forgetting I was stark naked.

"Why don't you get back into bed, Jack?" the driver of the police car strongly suggested. "Nothin' here that concerns you."

"Well, what the hell's happening?"

"You want me to haul your ass down to the station for indecent exposure?" he threatened. "Now get back in your house. It's just a dog, for Chrissake. Your neighbor's dog went and tangled himself up in his leash. Hung himself from the clothesline, all right? Now will you just get back inside, buddy, before we have a real problem here?"

Saturday

s long as I was up, I didn't want to waste the morning. At the same time my head began clearing, I was filled with a tremendous surge of energy. I wanted to do physical work. I wanted to sweat and get dirty. Even the pain in my toe began to subside and the thought of my bare foot in the grass or mud of the backyard struck me as therapeutic.

I threw on a pair of cutoff jeans and went outside. From the little cement stoop overlooking the patio, I surveyed the general condition of the backyard. I decided to mow the lawn, pull out the weeds growing through the seams in the brick patio, vacuum the swimming pool, trim the hedges, and plant the garden. If my toe didn't bother me, I might even borrow Otto's ladder and clean out the roof gutters.

It felt good to be outdoors with just a pair of shorts on. I sucked in my gut and stuck out my chest. A little breeze swept over my skin. The seven A.M. sun was strong and going to be stronger. I checked the state of my tan. Fair. Spotty. It would be deeper in a few hours.

The lawnmower was in the shed, but the sliding doors of the shed had come off their runners. I had to lift and push them in the same motion to get at the mower. And then when the mower was out, it wouldn't start. I felt as if strength alone would make the motor turn over. I pulled the cord ten times in quick succession, but nothing. I was sweating. The palm of my hand was red and my arm ached. Ten more times. I kicked it with my good foot. Ten more pulls.

I pulled the cord as hard as I could. It hadn't recoiled all the way, so the yank was effortless and caused me to lose my balance. But on the next pull I heard the motor try to turn over. Furiously I worked the cord until the engine fired and the roar drowned out the chirruping and early morning highway traffic.

69

Setting the mower in high gear, I guided it down toward the bottom of the backyard hill where the last owners had snugly set up the pool amid white pines on the right, a great oak behind, rosebushes along the front concealing the elevation of the redwood deck, and honeysuckle on the left which made the wire fence that separated my property from Otto's a beautiful boundary rather than an unfriendly eyesore.

Then I began to attack the rest of the grounds from in front of the rosebushes up the steep grade to the patio and the house itself. I steered the mower in parallel paths to the house instead of going up and down the hill. The vibrating handle felt powerful. I felt powerful holding it. Periodically I faced the mower behind me and held it at bay with one hand while I stooped down in its unfinished path to pick up one of the kid's toys and toss it onto an already mowed section of grass.

There was close to a month's growth, a good, tall, thick growth that dramatized the job; how much more rewarding it was to clip a foot instead of an inch, to clean a crusty dish rather than a pot that had just boiled eggs or spaghetti, to wash your own filthy ankles and grime-ringed wrists rather than merely give yourself a ritual rinse before dinner or bed. I liked letting things build up and then diving in over my head. Although it could be dangerous, I ran my business that way too, allowing papers to pile up, files to remain unclosed, unmade reports to come perilously close to their deadlines before plunging in for a day or two of nonstop work that cleared everything away. Suddenly I could see the top of my desk. Suddenly I could see the ground beneath the little forest of grass. A great feeling of accomplishment.

I loved the roar of the mower, the ticklingly long and then prickly short feel of the grass beneath my feet, the beating sun. I loved the self-absorbed privacy my effort spun around me as I threw myself heart and soul into the work. Steadily, dreamily, the incredible noise of the motor turned into a kind of silence.

Half the yard. Three quarters. The fringe around the patio and along the foundation of the house. Back down again. A second run at some of the rough, missed spots. And the impossible task of mowing away the lines between the paths. You couldn't get rid of them altogether, only move them. The traces had to be there, like the traces of the path a human being took. It would be quite an accomplishment if someone lived his allotted span without leaving behind a single record of his having existed. But the whole idea was one of those two-edged swords; how would anyone ever prove such an existence?

When I pushed the mower through the just-big-enough space between the large shade maple and the hedge-bordered patio wall, I caught a glimpse of my cat pawing at the breezeway screen. She wanted to come out. The birds, particularly, drove her crazy. Or the squirrels whenever they flew from the branches of the maple to the branches of the elm almost ten feet away. She was probably crying that eerie Siamese mating call that drove me crazy before I had her spayed, but I couldn't hear her over the roar of the motor.

Finally the bag was full of grass, and I had to dump it into the trash can. I detached it from the mower and shook the contents down to the bottom of the bag, enjoying the fresh green smell. I reached inside, digging my fingers into the grass. A toad's hind leg was in a handful of the grass I let run through my fingers.

"I wisht I had a lawn to mow."

Otto's voice startled me. He was standing on his side of the honeysuckle fence, staring at me blankly. He looked like a scarecrow against the background of huge stakes. He had turned his entire backyard into a vegetable garden, but the centerpiece was his rectangular tomato patch marked by tall gray wooden slats.

I honestly didn't know whether he was talking to me or to himself, and so I ignored him, figuring I would pretend I hadn't heard what he said.

I waited a moment or two, and when he didn't speak I dragged the canvas bag of grass around the side of the house to the front where the garbage cans were. I lifted the lid, dumped the grass inside, and remembered that today was Saturday, garbage day. So I took the two cans into the street at the end of the driveway. I wasn't sure I wanted to get rid of the evidence of my hard work, but I wasn't sure what I had in mind by keeping it.

Otto was still standing where I had left him. In his hands was his dog's leash, cut in half, which he kept winding and unwinding about his fingers. His gaze had remained unchanged.

I hardly knew him. We had been next-door neighbors but not close ones. There was a big difference in our ages. Otto was certainly in his sixties, maybe even in his early seventies, and we both suspected that, like our ages, everything else in our lives was equally far apart. We had only our land in common, and even that illustrated our differences; on one side of the honeysuckle was a well-tilled, carefully plotted vegetable garden, while on the other side was a hill full of broken, weatherworn toys leading to a store-bought swimmin' hole. His home life was centered on work. Mine seemed to center on amusement.

The little I knew about Otto had been more than enough to type him in my mind: his unshakable foreign accent; his heavily lined face and shiny bald head; his job as a teacher in the agricultural college (exactly what he taught I didn't know); his Sunday morning churchgoing; his idle threat that one of these hot nights don't be surprised if he and the missus jumpt the fence and dove into my pool; his frequent complaint about the shiftlessness of one of his sons who, for no reason at all, I believed was a drug addict; the tall, strappingly good shape Otto was in; his regular denunciation of my regular cigarette ("One of dese days you're goink to burn us all up, if dey don't kill you first like dey kilt my fodder"); the little tattoo on his forearm that told of his devotion to his mother and inspired images in my head of whistling bombs and grim-faced infantrymen slogging through Balkan mud; the restrained charm which surfaced when he was most restrained; the slight swagger; the earth under his nails; the geometric and almost religious purposefulness of his tomato patch; everything that was easily apparent about this now gaunt, bereaved scarecrow fiddling with his dog's noose/leash made me think of an aged Max von Sydow, a farmer-priest, an iron Wisconsinite rising with the sun, a man not to be distracted from his inner mission except when his wife, with her too loud and lilting "Otho," summoned him to start the barbecue briquettes. On the other hand, my portrait of Otto was painted from the several snapshots my mind had taken over the years, and it was possible that these pictures lied, that behind the honeysuckle and behind the stilted facade of the man there lived an entirely different person.

I hoped he would leave me alone as I picked up a hand spade and the small plastic flatbed of tomato plants he had given us and limped back outside to the area behind the pool, where our meager garden had been waiting since the first thaw, to plant the seedlings.

There was still a bit of tilling to do, rocks to get rid of, weeds to pluck out, soil to turn over before I could get my hands into the earth and dig holes for the tomato plants. I was amazed I knew what to do. All my life I'd been a city person and had resisted, I thought, embracing the duties that came with owning a house and land. But subconsciously I had learned more than I realized. It had been my dream to make enough money so that I never had to get my hands dirty with pipe rust or house paint or spackle or any of the countless and menial jobs one faced on weekends, yet here I was relishing a dirty, tiring, blister-raising farm chore. Me, who knew so much about the desires of strangers; I laughed to think how little I knew about myself.

"My dog kilt herself this morning, did you know?"

This time I couldn't ignore him, although he wasn't looking at me and seemed to be in a trancelike state of shock.

"I know. Terrible. How old was she?" I asked without stopping what I was doing.

But he didn't hear me, or else he didn't care to answer. He just went right on with his soliloquy as if I weren't there.

"She kept the birts away, you know. Yes, she did. Good girl."

"Christ," I muttered to myself.

"I still don't unnerstant how she did it. Maybe she was jumping up after a bluejay or somepin and went tru a loop or somepin in de leash?"

I could hear the cat crying now and tried to listen to her instead of Otto.

"Fourteen years we were togedder. She was almost a hunnert in dog years. But she was healty. Her teet were good. And she was always happy just to be runnin' in the yart, back and fort, not like some dogs who have to go prowlin' around in all de neighbors' garbage."

I kept trying to think of something to say that would snap him out of his trance, but I was afraid that then he'd want to strike up a conversation with me. I was even placing the rocks out of the garden rather than tossing them, so the noise wouldn't attract his attention. Why couldn't he just go inside and have himself a good cry?

"Fourteen years she was on de line and never a problem. She

must have jumpt to get at a birt," he convinced himself. And then he turned out of his trance and began to take stock of his vegetable garden. He bent down and felt some new lettuce leaves.

"I was goink to take her fishin' wit me. Let her run around widout de leash."

•

In a focus group interview designed to probe the feelings of widows and widowers about what kind of postburial services the cemetery could offer—and at what price, of course—the chipper people in the A group, the group selected on the basis of having been widowed for at least ten years regardless of remarriage (a mistake, I had thought, to lump together remarrieds with not), Group A talked easily about their tragedies, and every member was willing to shell out a small monthly amount in order to pay regular respect to their dearly departeds without having to pay regular visits to the graveyard. But Group B, the recently bereaved, those whose husbands or wives had left them within the last year, they still could not talk about it comfortably and, when they did manage to voice an opinion, invariably resented anyone else's planting a flower or placing a stone or commemorating certain important holidays. They resented anyone else's assuming their grief. But they did like most of the cemetery's ideas, such as a valentine adornment for the fourteenth of February, or a tiny crèche for the twenty-fifth of December. What Mr. Ballantyne had said, for example, symbolized the instinct of the group in general: "The valentine is a good idea, but I would rather just pay my wife a visit that day and maybe place a little token of my own on her grave."

He'd rather do it himself. He had to do it himself. And, just think, if Ballantyne didn't rhyme with valentine I might never have remembered the lesson of that focus group. I might have forced myself, like an insensitive landlord of the dead and buried, into poor Otto's private pathos.

Next Otto began slapping the side of his leg with the half leash. Gently. Nervously. Unconsciously, I guessed. Perhaps he was hammering home the fact of his dog's crazy death. It really was crazy. Hers was a case of absolutely accidental death. A freak accident on top of it all. I shook my head in ironic disbelief. There she was, completely and indulgently taken care of, leading the perfect dog's life. Good food, high-grade scraps from the barbecue, regular baths and visits to the vet, endless exercise up and down the backyard, fresh air, fondling, baby talk, all the things one would think would make a dog's life safe and sound and happily complete. Then with no warning, no detectable signal of sickness or insanity or any of the other things that happen to hundred-year-old dogs to prepare their masters for the end, she mysteriously, recklessly, maybe even discontentedly (if Otto was right about her frustrating leaps at a jaybird) managed to hang herself in a leash and a clothesline. It seemed to me that last leap of hers had to be a pretty desperate one. And a mile high for a dog.

Suddenly I realized I was saving vacuuming the pool for last, that the pool was like a glorious dessert you're willing to plod through a lousy dinner to get to. The end justified, even elevated, the means. It would feel good to have earned the refreshing promise of the glittering blue water, for after the planting and weeding and trimming and tedious job of vacuuming, I was going to throw myself into that cool water as if it were an oasis.

The slapping was becoming more pronounced. It was as if anger were being created out of the charged space between chain links and dungarees. I kept waiting for a spark to shoot out, and then another and another until a fiery energy existed that could then spread up Otto's arm or body to his head and explode into a catharsis of rage and grief. He was the kind of man who kept things bottled up inside, and one day those bottles would have to explode. I could almost see smoke coming out of his ears. I could nearly hear the shattering of glass.

The remaining ground was ready to be turned over. I dug at it with the hand spade and was relieved to find how easily it yielded to the blade. I turned the soil quickly, impatient to plant the tomatoes.

Without having to look his way, I could now hear Otto banging the metal leash against his thigh. I wondered if it hurt. The spade unearthed a worm that lay perfectly still, and I chopped it in two. Both ends began to wiggle. I prodded them with my finger to see if they'd crawl away from each other or toward each other, but before I got any results from the experiment I caught sight of Otto as he switched from beating his leg to whipping one of the tall gray slats with the leash. The leash was still long enough to wind itself around a stake when it landed, and Otto liked the idea that he could uproot the stake by yanking the leash back suddenly.

Let him go, I thought. Let him get it all out of his system.

Now the stakes were flying out of the ground in all directions as Otto spun and whipped through the patch like a human twister. Whatever he was shouting was unintelligible to me—maybe a curse from the old country, maybe his dog's name. Some stakes broke in half from the quick whip of the chain, others resisted the beating but always flew impassively out of their beds when Otto yanked them with his chain leash. They landed as far away as his patio, a testimony to the impassioned strength of the old man. One came cartwheeling over the honeysuckle fence and danced to a stop on the steps of the redwood deck leading to my pool. My cat was scampering from the screened door to the screened wall and back again, unable to decide which was a better vantage. When all the stakes were busted or uprooted, Otto went to work on the rest of his garden, destroying its perfect symmetry, dashing the groping life out of the rows of first, second, and close to final stage vegetation, shredding the leaves, pounding the newly formed earth wombs, severing the vines, lacing his fury into pods and stalks and fresh flowering buds.

The best thing for me to do, I decided, was nothing. Chances were there was no one else home at Otto's house or his wife would have come to his rescue, but still, unless he hurt himself, unless the chain smashed uncontrollably into his own face or he began to gasp and flutter from a heart attack, it was best to leave him alone. I told myself I'd keep one eye on him while I finished tilling and began to dig holes for the tomato plants.

At first I plotted the holes equidistantly, with the overall expanse of available good earth in mind. But soon I abandoned any plan and dug the holes wherever the ground looked prime. Otto's rage had quieted down a little, although he was still staggering through the yard searching for one more bit of growing green that might have escaped the unrelenting scythe of his fury.

By now, Otto was on his knees sobbing to himself, the great rain after the terrible windstorm. Sloppily I shoved the root balls into their holes, packing the dirt tightly around each one. The acidy scent of chlorine drifted my way and I took a deep, satisfying breath. I was filthy up to my knees and elbows. Sweat dripped into my eyes and off the tip of my nose. Soon it would all disintegrate in the magic underwater of the chlorinated pool.

I was feeling a little sorry for Otto, but at the same time I thought he had been foolish to let himself become so attached to a dog. There is less sadness over the loss of something that really is attached. Your appendix, for example. Or the umbilical. The half inch that makes certain noses too long. Bunions, warts, piles, hangnails, sunburn, dead teeth—mostly undesirable attachments, but nevertheless each was another fated good riddance to the wonderful equipment you were born with or you cultivated. They say you still feel an arm or a leg after it's amputated. Did Otto still feel his dog that way?

The hedge clippers were my favorite tool. Limping back to the garage, I pictured them, giant scissors. Surprising changes in scale had always thrilled me. Miniatures. Monsters. Big little things. Little big things. I took them off their nail and clipped at the musty air in the garage. The two blades clashed cleanly, producing a single swordfight sound that managed to echo slightly despite the poor acoustics. As I passed the breezeway door, the cat begged me to let her out.

Poor Otto was still slumped in the mess he had made, not about to pull himself together for a good while, I decided. But who had time for an old man crying over a hanged dog? I had work to do. Work work work.

There weren't many bushes, but they were thick and shapeless. It would take a good eye and a steady hand to clip them into a presentable form. I felt like a sculptor as I began trimming the bare branches first; they were bare because they had grown too fast to bear leaves. They had outstripped themselves, outgrown the universal plan intended for hedges.

What the hell were hedges anyway? I promised myself I'd look up hedges in the dictionary and considered how I'd like to shape them. My hedges grew like sprouts or cones, and the branches intersected between each bush, giving the retaining wall of the patio the semblance of an outer wall of greenery. But it would not be difficult to thin out the bushes and make each one distinct. Did I want a single hedge or several bushes? Unable to decide, I started by shaping the row as a single hedge, since that would allow me to change my mind. Which I did two bushes later. The problem was that the bushes really had been planted separately. Even though the branches interconnected, they did not form a solid table of leaves like those magnificent hedgerows in front of mansions. From any angle you could see that my bushes were planted approximately three feet apart and that they grew together, at the top, only because no one kept them in trim. But I would do right by them now. And I would notice, after separating the second bush from the third one, how much the first two, trimmed but still together, resembled a woman's torso. Mrs. P.'s big breasts to be exact.

The heat penetrated my back and shoulders as I hacked and clipped and sawed and tweezed and finally duplicated Mrs. P.'s body six times.

I looked back down at the pool and saw a sparrow light on the lid of the filter drum to take a drink from the little leak-fed puddle that had accumulated.

I laughed to think that I had tried to get the previous owners to lower their asking price on the house because of the pool. I had actually been upset that it was there. Everything else was so perfect, the upstairs, the downstairs, the basement, closet space, plumbing, heat, custom molding, window treatments, and then I looked out the enormous Andersen windows in the dining room and saw the sellers' two kids splashing around in a foot of green water. Immediately I resented having to fill the damn thing to a more respectable height, having to skim it, chlorinate it, vacuum it, cover it up in the winter, uncover it in the spring, set up the filtering system, take the filtering system apart, patch any liner leaks, worry that no one would drown, and probably face extraordinary water and electric bills which my projected budget was too inflexible to accommodate. But even more upsetting than discovering the pool was realizing that without it the asking price might have been more in line with what I wanted to spend. So I asked if they'd lower their price, seeing as how I didn't really want the pool. Or if they'd at least pay the cost of removing it. And they laughed as though I were kidding. Begrudgingly, I laughed, too, as though I had been kidding, and I paid their price. Now I'd sooner get rid of the house than that dazzling circle of blue water. Blue because the liner was blue. Actually the water was crystal clear.

I swam twenty laps every morning before I went to work. At night, when it got dark, I'd go down to the pool in nothing but a robe. I'd drop it to my ankles like one of those sharp-shouldered B-movie actresses and then lower myself into the blackness. It was always much colder at night, and I'd only dunk myself once or twice, swim two underwater strokes and back, before I'd have to climb out and wrap the heavy terry-cloth robe around my shivering. But in an instant I'd be warm again, too warm, my flesh would start to get sticky, and I'd slip in again for one more little swim. Later today I'd dive in.

.

The weeds growing out of the cracks in the patio amazed me. How could these slender, frail blades force the bricks apart? I plucked the tallest ones and realized I would need something to get at the short clumps. The hand spade, maybe. I went back down behind the pool to the garden. My toe still hurt. It looked like it might be broken; it bent away from the other four. I put all the pressure I could on the inside of my foot, keeping the possibly broken toe slightly raised.

All I could do with the hand spade was force an incision, then I had to dig at the roots with my fingers because the blade was too broad. I wanted to prolong the labor before the relief of the pool, so I continued plucking and cutting and digging for several more minutes until finally, though I hadn't recemented the seams and cracks, the reddish bricks did look a little better; where the lepers of the grass had divided up the patio, there were now thin neat lines of dark brown earth.

Done. I looked up into the sun. Not yet noon.

A bird flew over the pool and dropped the cherry it had picked from Otto's tree. The cherry sank to the bottom, endless ripples marking the spot.

Closing the entrance gate behind me, I climbed up the three steps of the redwood deck. From that height the neighbors could see me if they wanted to look through the trees, but the guy who was always playing his radio too loud must have been away, and the two old ladies who lived together were not sharply overlooking a neighborhood kid who had to put up with their finicky supervision to earn his dollar for mowing their backyard, and those young kids who lived behind the little wood that insulated the right side of my property were not carrying on in that distinctly teenage chatter of giggles and shouts, shouts and giggles.

I turned off the filtering system. After disconnecting the intake hose from the skimmer, I connected it to the long vacuum hose. Then I turned the filter on again and watched the enormous plastic snake attempt to unwind itself as the water coursed through. I controlled the vacuum by its long, aluminum handle; I held it like a lance.

The most efficient way to clean was to inch the vacuum head along the bottom of the pool as methodically and as slowly as possible so as not to stir up the algae and specks of decomposed leaves. Even though the instrument worked like a Hoover, except there was no disposal bag, you'd do better not to race it along the floor. In fact, you couldn't, because of the resistance of the water. But I had no patience. Certainly not the kind of patience that would make me go over and over the same spot, determined to suck up the re-settled impurities the first go-over missed. Instead I pushed and pulled with all my might, constantly forcing the vacuum head to a new area. If the pool doctor could see me now she'd spank me.

She was tough. She made me feel as though my dinky little pool was her whole life. Water samples. Algae tests. Prescription chemicals. More samples. And that pugnacious attitude of hers, her feisty way of referring to my pool as "that baby." "How's that baby doin'?" "This'll knock all the rot outta that baby." "Ya gotta keep that baby clean."

I was intimidated by her dedication. Of all the things to devote yourself to, of all the things on earth worth studying, analyzing, deciphering, purifying, controlling, imagine this dead-end-kid of a woman biologist picking my little backyard pool. And yet she did. Whenever I walked into her shop, she remembered my name and my water. "I know, I know, that baby needs some more algicide."

What impressed me most was her absolute refusal to go anywhere near a pool that wasn't under her personal care. "I've seen what that water's got in it, mister. Under the microscope. Ya got dead skin and mucus and uric acid and sputum and that's just for starters. I'm not even talkin' algae and larvae and all the crap you can see with the naked eye."

With my naked eye I saw only a few acorns, a few leaves, the cherry, and what looked like harmless clouds floating up from the swath of the vacuum head. There was an assortment of dead and dying insects on the surface, but who cared? When I attached the intake hose to the skimmer, they'd all be recirculated into oblivion.

If I listened to the pool doctor, I wouldn't swim in anything but amniotic fluid. I sucked up the leaves and acorns, but the cherry was too big.

The pool doctor knew so much about water I was afraid it was her only passion. Isn't that what happens when you're all-consumed, you have to give up all else? Mrs. P., for example, would never devote herself to anything that would interfere with her being the kind of woman a man could truly appreciate. The pool doctor, I worried, would smear your love on a slide and slip it under her microscope before she'd let it into her body. She wouldn't even have to unbutton her lab coat. Yet she did take care of my pool; she made sure I didn't drown in my own sputum. In her funny Leo Gorcey way, she was passionate about that.

Good enough. I disconnected the vacuum and hooked up the skimmer, which immediately swallowed a drowning wasp. The wasp fought, but the suction was too powerful.

I spread a towel along the pool edge of the deck, sat down on it, and dangled my feet in the water. The weightlessness made my toe feel good. Half the pool was sunlit; the other half looked colder and less enticing even though I was hotter than I could ever remember.

I lit a cigarette. Seven more minutes of filth and heat and un-relieved exhaustion. I knew it would take seven minutes because a focus group interview I once conducted showed that the average time a smoker spent with each cigarette was eight minutes. Then when I compared myself to the average, I found I was quicker by a full minute.

While I smoked, I unbuttoned and unzipped my shorts, wriggled out of them without getting up, and draped the towel over my private parts. Just being naked out-of-doors made my penis twitch and stiffen; I could see it move under the towel. When I was through with the cigarette, I pinched off the light and brushed it through the slats in the deck; then I flicked the filter twenty or thirty feet away into the woods.

The trick was to stand up with the towel wrapped around my waist and then drop it and dive into the pool in the same motion. At most a snoopy neighbor would catch a quick glimpse of my ass, or, depending on the vantage and the strength of his or her binoculars, the tip of my flapping penis. Once I was in the water, no one could see a thing unless he or she were right by the pool. But even that wouldn't embarrass me. There was something entirely different, something comfortably distorted and unreal, about being seen through the surface of the water. It was as if I were a fish of some kind, a natural creature of my four-foot-deep habitat. It was only when a fish was hooked and pulled up out of the water that it minded being watched. That embarrassed it to death.

As hot as I was, I had to work up the courage to plunge in. I knew that the coldness that swept across my calves just above the point where they were submerged was a false indication of the temperature. Still, I worried. Also I worried about whether or not the condition of my toe would inhibit me from pushing off the deck smoothly. Or, should the dive go well, if my toe would hurt a lot. I might even cause more damage. Permanent damage.

Of course, it was all a game. I dragged up every excuse for not wanting to take the plunge. The entire morning had been planned to build to this moment.

Finally I stood up, held the towel closed around me, braced myself, dropped it, paused an instant or two, then dove in. The water hit me, slid over me, chilled me, warmed me, held me under, lifted me back up.

It could never have been as wonderful as I had anticipated, but it surprised me in other ways. I had the sensation of flying. My penis immediately shrunk to its littlest size. The water seemed to finger the inside of my ass. Every organ in my body felt more relaxed. My heart beat slower and louder. My lungs floated in my chest. My stomach expanded.

I looked at myself as I drifted underwater, using only my hands and feet to keep from surfacing or gliding into the wall; every hair on my body was distinct, the dirt decomposed and disappeared, my skin looked eerily white, almost incandescent. Suddenly I realized that my underwater posture was my true posture, that without the pressure of gravity, society, clothing, the influence of celebrated stances, the dignity of evolution, that without anything but the free force of life, this was what I really looked like, middle slightly out of joint, legs bent, hairs wavering, digits spread, balls dangling, penis cowering—this was the true, physically impossible me.

I enjoyed touching myself, running my hands along my thighs, rubbing my legs together, stroking both arms at the same time, cupping my genitals, then spreading my legs and letting everything dangle freely. It was as if I were two different people. I loved touching and being touched, watching and being watched. And there was the sense, too, of a third presence. But no matter where I turned to look for her, she darted behind my vision. All I could see for sure was a faint motion of the water in her wake.

There was the cherry. But I didn't have enough breath left to get it. I had to come up for air. I surfaced on the side of the pool nearest to Otto's yard. He was gone.

The water came up just past my waist and kept resettling around me as I waded through the pool. The half of me that was submerged appeared more graceful, more ethereal. Leaning back against the curved wall, I searched the waters, trying to spot the phantom mermaid. But she was too slippery for me, too quick to change form, or conceal herself in the imaginary seaweed, or cling to the very bottom where my vision was the most distorted.

Then she made her entrance as I knew she would, her underwater hair streaming like fire, her face showing no trace of the deep. No puffed cheeks. No pained eye slits. No difficulty breathing or seeing. Her mouth made soundless words.

"Come down to me," she mouthed. She was directly below me; her writhing phantom form and my slowly but surely enlarging penis both in the same line of vision. I saw my hand encircle the semi-erection, squeeze it, twist it, pull it, flutter away like some grotesque anemone. She began to materialize like a photographic print, and I saw she was swaddled in silken silver skin; she was armless; she had iridescent scales; there were wine-red markings;

there were hieroglyphics beneath one breast that I tried to decipher. But I had to get closer. My reflected self was fully dressed, a white sport coat, a royal blue shirt open at the collar, a naked hand that combed my hair, but there was a wide white ring of no sunburn on the third finger.

"Come down to me, my love."

I swam down to meet her, diving through the image of myself, hurtling toward the silver and wine red ghost.

"I've come from the farthest shores, the ancient seas, the bays of our beginnings."

The blurry hieroglyphics slowly came into focus. I'VE . . .

"I've come from the sparse basins and muddy deltas of Mesopotamia."

. . . COME . . . all that prevented me from reading them was the bubbling my own thrashing caused, but I had to keep myself under.

"I've come from the headlands, spits, and jetties of lost princedoms by the sea."

. . . A LONG WAY . . .

"I've come from time and man and primal soup."

. . . BABY.

Suddenly the entire pool was in a turmoil. Still underwater, I wheeled around as fast as I could. From amidst the million wild bubbles and swirling abstract blue there came the real sound and real sight of a horrible monster: a half dog–half man.

I tried to run up to the surface. My lungs gave out. I swallowed and spit blue bubbles. The thing came at me; the water held me down. Finally my head broke through and I rubbed frantically at my eyes.

It was Otto. His arms and shoulders and shining head seemed to be suspended over the edge of the pool. His dog floated just beyond his reach.

•

Something wasn't right. But I was determined not to dwell on whatever it was. After all, I had a date with an angel.

Otto had returned to his backyard. I peeked at him through my kitchen window. He walked around slowly, dispassionately, inspecting the wreckage as if someone else had caused it. Then he went inside. His dog drifted along the curved wall of the pool. From the kitchen you could not tell the brown and black mass was a dog, nor could you see it drift. You knew it drifted when you looked back and saw that the dark shape in the clean blue circle of water was not where it had just been.

My stomach rumbled, and I remembered that I hadn't eaten anything since peanuts at the bar after work last night. I opened the refrigerator. Eggs, cheese, onions, salami, I ransacked the refrigerator, filling my arms with everything that looked good; then I spun gracefully around and kicked the door shut the way Fred Astaire would have done it. It felt good to have an appetite and know I could satisfy it. My hands worked automatically, without my having to think of what seasonings to use, how to combine the ingredients, whether to spread mustard or mayo or ketchup, how thick to slice the onion, whether to toast the bread or not. Even when the phone rang, my hands reacted before I did. They wiped each other with a paper towel, nestled the receiver between my cheek and shoulder, and went right back to work.

I began to pay attention halfway through the caller's opening speech.

". . . I have people here on staff that I have to pay. I could have tried to set up another appointment if your wife had only had the courtesy to call me and say she couldn't make it. Perhaps she doesn't understand, but when we test a child we design the programs specifically for his or her needs. It's not as simple as you may think. We had people and equipment and time especially set aside for your son and only your son. I hope there's a good reason why no one showed up this morning. It was the last test, you know. The most important test of the entire series."

The good reason composed itself in my heart which thumped madly, bravely, jubilantly with each wicked word of the white lie.

"Yes. Well. Ahh, she went to the market for a quart of milk. That was Thursday. But you know how they always keep the milk in the farthest corner of the store. She probably noticed a few more items on her way back to the checkout counter. I'm sure she'll be home any minute. Of course, there are all those stories about husbands or wives who go to the store and that's the last you ever hear of them, but I'm sure she'll be back any minute. I'll have her call you the minute she walks in."

Once again my hands took over. They hung up the phone before I could hear whether or not the professor was satisfied.

I smeared on mustard and ketchup and no one said "ugh." One of the blessings of being grown-up is having the freedom to eat what and when you please. Surely the big bowl of leftover roast beef was scheduled for another main course, but somehow I felt no compunctions about nibbling at it, even taking a slice for my sandwich although that would leave an insufficient amount for four dinners.

The phone rang again. This time I reacted quickly, picking it up with my side of the conversation already calculated. The caller was surprised and distressed to hear my voice. What I told her was not reassuring.

"She's dead," I said matter-of-factly. "They're all dead. The house exploded Thursday."

"You couldn't have spoken to her," I countered. "What time was it? Maybe I'm mistaken; maybe it was yesterday that the house exploded. You can understand how upset I've been. You never saw anything like it; everything's a complete ruin. An overload, that's what caused it. She had the washer and dryer running—the little one wet his bed again. Plus all the air conditioners were going full blast, plus she was vacuuming up something the big one spilled, plus the oven was on, the kids' record player, my stereo, the toaster —and then one of them decided to turn on the television and KAPOW. There was a chain reaction. The washer blew which made the boiler blow which set the kitchen off . . . when I got home I found the refrigerator door floating in the pool. The phone's just about the only thing left."

"What am I going to do? I have to talk to her. She told me to call before I did anything."

"Maybe I can help," I offered rather decently, deciding against the onion because I had a date with an angel.

"What's the difference? It's too late for me. I'm sitting here with the gas on and a bottle of Thorazines. You can't help me."

I didn't know who she was, only that I had heard her name around the house once or twice. She was probably a mother and I asked her where her children were, but she ignored my question and began sobbing. Obviously there was nothing I could do. "Good-bye," I said.

At the office the phone would start ringing at about ten o'clock. It would ring in assorted business till noon, take a lunch break, then start again at two and go on until four. I wondered if there were as predictable a routine at my house, too. No calls all morning. Then it begins a little before noon, and so on, whatever the distribution. Running the house could be sort of like running a business, couldn't it?

I was feeling quite pleased with myself, almost heady. I set up my lunch on the dining room table. The plate was overflowing with my favorite things to eat, potato chips, sandwich pickles, hot peppers—the Dagwood itself. An ice-cold beer stood by in its sweating can. I was particularly pleased with the way I had handled the calls. Nearly giggling as I remembered, word for word, what I had said, I forced the dining room chair past whatever was leaning against its leg. I was glad my secretary hadn't been there to answer the calls. Now that I had decided to go to work and contact Mrs. P., everything I said or did or ate seemed to fit into the flow of things. My mood, already colored by the anticipation of my date, needed periodic priming, exercise almost. The calls had served that purpose, as would the sandwich. There was absolutely no doubt that I was feeling pretty chipper.

Halfway through my sandwich, the phone rang again, and I was tempted to ignore it. But more and more I felt that I was caught in a ridiculous plot, a Restoration drama, a bedroom farce, a musical comedy. There was an undercurrent of frivolous music I felt compelled to keep time to. To keep the action rolling along I had to answer the phone. I couldn't disregard the cue; but my answer, how I handled myself, what I said, the tone of my voice, all that was up to me.

"Hello," I said. "Before you say anything," I said, "my wife is not here. She's gone. As far as I can determine there are three possibilities: she ran off with the parcel post man, succumbing at last to the irresistible way he has of leaping off his truck before it comes to a full stop in a manner not unlike heroes of the untamed West who dismount, hitch, and kick open a swinging saloon door before the sweat dripping off Tony or Champion or Silver or Trigger or Topper hits the dust; or else she was called away, quite suddenly to the Small Talk Convention in Zenith, having been named chairperson of the What-Detergent-Do-You-Use committee; or else she's out back hard at work over her anvil, forging foolproof shackles the exact circumference of my flaccid . . ."

Just as I was about to say "take your pick," I realized that the voice on the other end had gone on talking as if I couldn't be heard.

"Your donation," it continued, "not only entitles you to the four monthly magazines, the biweekly, and the daily newspapers I've described, but also you will receive a window sticker identifying you and every member of your household as contributors to the Animal Shelter Program. This sticker is quite large and features a colorful illustration of the family of domestic pets, including dog, cat, parakeet, gold fish, hamster, and rabbit."

An instant before I realized that the voice was recorded, I foolishly demanded to know if it had heard anything I'd just been saying.

There was a pause, a click, and the owner of the voice herself got on, asking in one breath whether there were any questions and to what exact address did I want monthlies, biweeklies, dailies, and sticker sent.

"There is a woman," I said calmly, "who is sitting in a gas-filled room with a bottle of Thorazines in her hand. I'm sure she'd be thrilled to talk to you. I'm sure she'd be thrilled to talk to anyone. Why don't you give her a buzz and ask if she'd like a picture of a hamster?"

I slammed the phone back angrily, but took out all my rage on the next bite of my sandwich, which my teeth tore off savagely.

I ate the rest of my lunch standing, impatient to get ready and get out, but still feeling jim-dandy. I was still moving, I thought, like Fred Astaire, still making every move as though it were choreographed. There was still that haunting music-hall melody in the air, that drum roll/slide whistle accompaniment that crackled to life when I sent the crumbs from the top of the dishwasher into the sink with one flamboyant sweep of my hand, or when I bumped a cupboard door shut with my head as I was passing, or when I flung my empty plate into the sink like a Frisbee and flinched at the sound of breaking china. The music carried me into the bathroom, where I took a good, long look at myself in the mirror. My hair was thick with chlorine, my eyes bloodshot. I needed a shave, a shower, the works. I needed to lose ten pounds. I needed a bigger chin.

I smiled at myself. Beneath the stubble and chlorinated hair and red eyes and filthy nails and sweating, dirt-streaked arms, chest, shoulders, legs, there was a pretty dapper fellow.

With the retractable blade of my nail clippers, I dug first into the caked filth wedged between my nails and the raw flesh of my fingertips. The dirt popped out easily, in little strings and clumps. The most satisfaction came when one gouge of the blade drove out the entire line of dirt; it reminded me of how every once in a while you got lucky and could devein a shrimp with a single yank, like pulling one of those perforated tabs on a box top.

I checked my toe. The pain was still there but it had reached a higher, less annoying pitch. I realized that I was still keeping pressure off it, and when I rested my foot on the ledge of the sink I saw why. The toe pointed east. It was redder than the others. When I touched it lightly, it throbbed with electric pain. I put my foot down and waited for the aching current to travel so far beyond its course it would disappear, leaving only the original little pulse of discomfort. I prepared my face for shaving. What was I going to wear?

My light blue pants for sure, I decided, massaging a bit of pre-shave into my beard. There were two, possibly three, shirts that went with the pants, one of which would depend on the jacket I chose and another of which would depend on the one pound I gained or lost from day to day. If I gained it, then the pink shirt would pull slightly at the buttons along my paunch.

Shaving was always easier in the middle of the day. The razor sailed along my face, clinging and dipping in and out of the contours like a roller-coaster car, plowing the lather into hair-flecked mounds that hung from my jawbone and then plopped silently into the sink. Perhaps my tennis shoes would be comfortable. Or my sandals. Yes, the open-toed sandals would be perfect. But how would they look with my light blue pants, my pink or white or dark blue shirt, and my white sport coat or navy blue blazer? Too hot for the blazer. That settles that. Besides, white would set off the tan I saw I had as I wiped the last traces of shaving cream from my cheeks and neck.

The only way the sandals would fit, I thought, was if I sacrificed the light blue pants. But I knew I wouldn't do that. They were, I reassured myself as I turned on the shower, a perfect blue for the occasion. Serenely blue. Casually blue. The color of Paul Newman's eyes. The pants were the one thing that was certain. The rest would have to be built around that certainty.

I stepped into the shower and watched the ingrained dirt resist the jetting water. The phone rang.

I was getting used to being interrupted. I was also getting used to prancing around the house with a certain daring abandon—for me. I slid back the shower door and dripped all the way into the kitchen. There was an extension phone in the bedroom just across the hallway from the bathroom, but I preferred the longer route. A sexy chill ran through me as I passed by the wide-open Andersen windows. There was something thrilling about being caught in an innocent, private moment; it was like being caught in a Greek myth. As I stood stark naked in the kitchen, about to answer the phone, my glistening back to the kitchen door, I imagined a visit from one of the baby-sitters from the neighborhood: she stops by to retrieve her composition book and can't help but see me through the window panes. She's too astonished to take her finger off the doorbell. Ring. Ring. Ring. I turn and face her and her mouth falls open. Still her finger is frozen to the bell. Ring. Ring. Ring. Having been legitimately interrupted while I was taking a perfectly respectable shower after a long morning of hard work, I am completely nonchalant. This is, after all, my house. In it I can dress or undress as I please. Certainly I can be surprised by a visitor without anyone's suspecting that I planned it that way. I walk casually to the door. Ring. Ring. Ring. I open the door. The baby-sitter cannot speak. She cannot unstick her eyes from the center of my body. Ring. Ring. Ring.

I answered the phone. To my double amazement, it sounded like one of the baby-sitters, and at the same time the front doorbell rang.

"Who? Beth? Hold it just a second, someone's at the door."

I peeked through the living room window and saw a young boy standing at the door. Suddenly I was ashamed to be naked. I went behind the door and opened it so it hid me. Just my head stuck out.

"Paperboy," he said.

What did he want? What was he doing here?

"It's a dollar twenty."

"Oh. Right. A dollar twenty."

I ran to the bedroom and found two dollar bills. But as I came back into the living room, I saw that I had left the front door open. The paperboy was just standing there looking through the screen door, which was still shut. I hurried into the bathroom, wrapped a towel around my middle, and brought him his money.

"Keep the change."

"Thanks," he said, and as he turned and headed for his bike I was sure I heard him giggle.

Beth. I shut the door, ran to the kitchen, pulled off the towel, used it to dry my hair, picked up the phone.

"Sorry. Beth?"

"Yes. I'm from camp. I just wanted to make sure your wife knows about Monday."

"What about Monday?"

"She's supposed to be one of the chaperones on the trip to Kiddieland."

"Of course," I said, warming to Beth's friendly voice, "she's been talking about it all week. Every other word out of her mouth has been Kiddieland, Kiddieland."

"Well, I guess she knows what time to be here and everything. And she said she was going to bring snacks for all the campers in my group."

I couldn't tell whether or not she thought I was home all alone, but Beth seemed perfectly willing to give me the information, no questions asked.

"And just you wait'll they sink their cute little kiddie teeth into them snacks. Shrimp remoulade. Marinated artichoke hearts. Guacamole and tostadoes. Quiche Lorraine. Eggs à la Russe. Mushrooms à la Greque. Egg rolls. Rollmops. Night and day she's been slaving over a hot fire, a dirty sink, an oily cutting board, she's been whisking, mixing, beating, pounding, shaping, stuffing, rolling, grinding, mincing, dicing, salting, peppering, tasting, basting, cooling, simmering, creating a smorgasbord, an antipasto, a puu puu platter nonpareil, fondue on the ferris wheel, Swedish meatballs on the wild mouse, clams casino on the carousel. Believe me, Beth, she'd never let those kids down."

The instant I hung up the phone it rang again.

"Is the lady of the house in?" It wasn't a machine this time, but the woman's voice was inhumanly officious.

"No. Yes. Uh, yes and no."

"I'll try again later; this is in reference to a clothing drive for hydrocephalic children." And she hung up.

I was sure she would call again. People like her always did. In fact, they would all call again. Beth, the animal shelter lady, ole suicidus interruptus, the professor. It was just a matter of time. After Kiddieland there'd be Pubertyland and Teenagerland. When enough time went by, or if pet brutality suddenly started grabbing the daily and biweekly headlines, Miss Hamster would run the tape again and stand by in person to clinch the sale. Of course, some things would change, I conceded, stepping back into the shower. Next time the professor would be uncomfortably optimistic about his findings. He'd try and make me, and himself, look on the bright side, knowing damned well it was just a con and feeling damned stupid that a man of his position had to hawk hope like some half-mad machine man. I couldn't wait to get dressed and get out.

Mood swings. What amazing mood swings. One minute I was waltzing through the house like a Disney character and the next minute the walls seemed to be closing in on me. Something outside of myself seemed to be in control of my emotions. Like the weather. Like a national tragedy. When Kennedy was killed there was a national mood swing. And when his brother was killed, it blew the shit out of that motivational sensory machine out in L.A.

Five hundred run-of-the-mill Americans were seated in a theatre to watch a Mr. Magoo cartoon while their hands were wired to a reaction dial they themselves could control; all they had to do was move the dial to *Enjoyable, Fairly Enjoyable,* or *Unenjoyable.* Probably five hundred thousand people before them had suffered through the identical cartoon and established a consistent, reliable standard of reaction. But in the wake of the assassination, the monitoring device was stumped for two months. Twenty different run-of-the-mill audiences refused to *enjoy* a stigmatized runt walking through a plate glass window even though they were supposed to. Even though their predictably average reaction would have enabled them to qualify for the real tests: which deodorant seemed more appealing? which antacid? whose face? whose voice?

Whenever I thought about the technical advances in the research industry, it excited me. Invariably I began to think of my own little projects, small by comparison, but a respectable part of the blossoming science. Sure there were those knee-jerk romantics who insisted that research, more than anything else, was dehumanizing the already inhuman business world and, even worse, spreading to other fields, vulnerable ones like education and the popular arts. But at least my own particular business still relied heavily on the human touch, on personal contact, group interplay, individual opinion. Most of the idiosyncratic data had to be filtered out of final reports or simply represented a fixed margin of error, but dammit, that wasn't my fault.

I knew I wouldn't relax until I got to my office, until I sat behind my desk and leafed through tape transcriptions, or ruled a graph, or catalogued an apparent jungle of indistinguishable responses. I could feel the papers in my hands; the neat black type re-created the hour-long lives of the group members. In an hour, one hour, I knew them. Knew them better than they knew themselves. After all, I knew what they really meant by their casual remarks. And what those remarks could mean to my clients. And if the remarks were encouraging and the clients were aggressive, the innocent statements made by the group members could very well revisit them in the form of a man's moisturizer or a rhinestone-handled screwdriver for women. At first I held the power of the dreams of fifty interviewees, who took twelve dollars each and a few finger sandwiches in return for letting me put them under my one-way glass. But then, by extrapolation, I held the power of the dreams of millions. I was not kidding myself. Millions. And every one of them, unless a presidential candidate got shot, could be counted on to laugh in the same spots at that stupid cartoon.

I wasn't aware that the phone had been ringing again until it stopped. I stood outside the shower and waited. If it was family, the phone might ring again in the time it took to redial. Family would figure someone had to be home, and blame no answer on a wrong number. It was easier to live with a mistake in dialing than the thought that flesh and blood didn't care enough to inform you ahead of time of his whereabouts. But the phone did not ring.

Thinking about work had raised my spirits again; I could feel my mood change as I plugged in the blow dryer. I was moving as quickly as I could, not wanting to waste a single step or motion. I'd never been one to lounge around like a zombie when there was something I had to get done. Years of getting ready for work between 6:30 A.M. and 7:15 A.M. had resulted in unconscious shortcuts. Even though I wouldn't dry my hair until after dressing, I plugged in the gun while I was in the bathroom so it would be ready for me. When I went to the chest of drawers on the far side of the bedroom to select a shirt, I took my wallet, keys, a handkerchief, two subway tokens, and exact change for two newspapers from the top drawer and tossed it all onto the bed; that way I wouldn't have to go all the way back around the bed to the dresser for these pocket items after I put on my pants, saving myself four or five little steps.

I unwrapped the dark blue shirt, making sure the collar was unstarched, though if it weren't, what could I do? I had already decided on the dark blue to go along with the light blue pants and white sport jacket. I had bought the shirt on sale at an irregular-clothing outlet somewhere in Cleveland when a business trip stretched an extra day and I found myself short one shirt. The color was so attractive, the shopkeeper had had it hanging in the window to draw attention.

It looked fine as I buttoned the sleeves and the front, rakishly leaving the top two buttons open to reveal a glimpse of my moderately hairy chest.

I whistled "Got a Date with an Angel" as I posed in the shirt and nothing else in front of the dresser mirror. My penis peeked out of the tails, and it pleased me to see how big it looked with only its head showing. I whistled some more. Just the other day I had been trying to teach someone the mechanics of whistling and had run into a lot of trouble. There were no easy words to describe the positions of tongue and teeth and lips and the way you had to expel air. It occurred to me that a person either knew how to whistle or didn't. Either you stumbled onto it by accident one lucky day, or you worked at it and worked at it and happened, again accidentally, to get it right, and then you had to remember what it was that you did. There were people who could only master one note, others who were never even able to muster that much skill. But to me whistling seemed so natural, so simple and true. No words or problems with phrasing to get in the way. It was the closest we humans could come to being a pure instrument of expression, I thought, slipping into my shorts.

I pulled on one leg of the light blue pants very carefully so as not to put any pressure on my toe, tucked in the dark blue shirt, and threaded the belt loops with a white rope belt that started with a length of neutral leather and ended with a shiny brass buckle.

More than anything, I wanted to wear my new white shoes with the ripple soles. After taking them out of their soft cloth shoebag, I attempted to put weight on my right foot but had to stop immediately because of the pain in my toe. It was obvious that I wasn't even going to be able to get a sock over that foot. The slightest pressure shot long, dull pain from the toe right up through my heart. The rhythm of my natural pulses, my heartbeat, the coursing of my blood, the expansion and contraction of my lungs, the peristaltic movement of my insides, the tiny ticking of my temples were all thrown off, slowed, made to throb in terrible tempo with the spondees of pain emanating from my toe. No way to keep whistling "Got a Date with an Angel" while "All Alone" is tromboning through your body. What I had to do was cut an opening in one white shoe. As long as one foot was properly dressed I'd look okay.

I took the shoe downstairs to my basement workbench, secured it in a vise, and proceeded to customize the supple white leather with a crosscut saw. I sawed at an angle so I could preserve as much of the front of the shoe as possible. The opening was a little ragged, but the idea worked.

I had to ease my toe into the half shoe very delicately. Even so, it hurt. Finally I settled my whole foot in.

Because of the fine, soft, spotless, white leather and the smartly dressed drape of my light blue pant leg, which broke just above the ankle in perfect accordance with a classic law of fashion, I looked as if I must have the gout or some other rich ailment that catches you by the toe. My two feet might have looked foolish if it weren't for the flash and style of the rest of my outfit. I looked as though I had had an accident befitting a man of such apparent fine taste: a late night mishap on the sleek deck of my yacht perhaps, a wrong-footed landing at the end of a sky dive, a skiing blunder in Chile, jungle rot picked up on photographic safari.

I filled my pants pockets, took out the white sport jacket, which was still wrapped in the cleaner's protective plastic, hung it on the door to the closet, and returned to the bathroom to dry my hair.

But while I had been sawing off the toe of my shoe, my hair had dried funny. It stuck out in every direction and would not comb into place. With my hands I wet my hair again until the radicals were smoothed into conformity and my hairdo looked like Prince Valiant's. Except around the ears, of course. I had held out for years on the very long hair issue, and now a longish but neat trim was in fashion again. Even women were cutting their hair short. The girls in Group A had echoed each other's feelings precisely. "It's easier to manage when it's short. Especially in the summertime."

"It dries fast and never looks messy."

"I don't have to sleep on curlers every night and spend hours in front of the mirror the next day."

All good, practical, commonsense reasons. The older I got and the more I learned and the better I understood the significance of my findings, the surer I felt that life was simply a matter of practicality. Underneath the surface differences, we all just want to do what's easiest and most comfortable and most natural. I aimed the blow gun at my head and pulled the trigger.

The hot jet blew bald spots wherever I pointed it and made me see myself on the prow of a sloop or in the cockpit of a fighter plane or hurtling down the Acapulco cliffside in search of pearls the size of baseballs. Moving. I felt myself moving.

My hair dried but uncombed, I went into the bedroom and slipped into my white jacket, carefully laying the dark blue collar of my shirt over the white lapels. I smoothed down the collar, making it fit the contours of the jacket without showing a single wrinkle. Because the jacket was less formfitting, it pulled the clinging collar points away from each other, exposing a bigger, sexier vee of bare chest.

I whistled myself back to the bathroom mirror and began to comb my hair. At crucial stages, when I had to refine the frayed front of my part where it disappeared into my forehead, for example, my whistling stopped. My pursed lips froze for a moment or two, I held my breath, and then when the hairs were in place, I breathed again and whistled again.

It was during one of the frozen pauses that I recognized the vision. White jacket, dark blue shirt open at the collar, hand combing hair, everything just as I had seen it reflected in the waters of my pool. The image had frightened me then, but now it seemed innocent. The wide band of untanned skin on the third finger of my left hand was not as sinister as it had appeared through the blue rippling of the liner-tinted water.

My hair fell into the design of its cut, and my lips unfroze, and my song tea-kettled forth, and I refused to dwell on whatever it was that was trying to undermine my bright, tuneful, Hollywood set of a Saturday afternoon.

One last once-over in the mirror: left side, right side, front, back, neckline, shoulders, wrinkles, stray hairs, specks of dirt, traces of shaving cream, pin dot clots of blood, nose hairs, food caught in teeth, none, good, fine, wipe, good, gone, nice, out.

Even with my sawed-off shoe it hurt to walk, and I found myself trying out different limps to ease the pain. The best of them was more of a half goose-step. I simply used the heel only of my right foot, keeping the toes stuck up in the air like a rooster's comb. It was a strain on the heel, and unconsciously I kept reverting to my natural step. But the pain was a reminder, and lapses came further and further apart.

I set my watch to the railroad station regulator in the living room, found my keys on top of the liquor cabinet along with a nearly empty bottle of bourbon, made sure all the lights were out, and goose-stepped toward the back door.

That must have been when I decided to take the guzzler instead of my little red flivver of a train car. I didn't really remember debating the point, but when I got out to the driveway somehow the decision was already made. I'd move Mama Car into the street and use Papa Car to get me to the train station.

I hardly ever drove Papa Car anymore. It had become the family car, too roomy and smooth and powerful to just sit in a lot all day at the train station. Mama Car was perfect for that. It rattled around like a scooter with loose bolts, barely getting me back and forth, and sounding almost humanly out of breath when it coasted to either of its two daily stops.

I squeezed in behind the wheel and turned the ignition key. There was no other sound. Again. Just the click of the key.

I tried the lights and the radio. They both worked, which meant the battery was charging.

I released the emergency brake, shifted into neutral, and got out. Now I had to huff and puff and push Mama Car out of the driveway safely to the curb. I put my weight into the driver's side doorjamb and got her rolling.

With one hand on the steering wheel and the other on the jamb, I moved Mama Car slowly, slowly toward the street at the hardest angle the wheel would allow. The tires crunched over the pebbles in the driveway and I thought about that happening to my bare toes if I let Mama Car get out of control.

When there was enough space between the two cars for me to push from Mama Car's front end, I took off my jacket, laid it on the front seat of Papa Car, and limped back to Mama's front bumper. Sitting on Papa Car's trunk, I placed my heels on Mama's bumper and forced my legs to their full extension. Mama jiggled and rocked and finally rolled back a few feet.

Slowly but steadily, Mama reversed along the wheel arc until she was in the street, her nose sticking too far out.

I had to park Mama Car manually, inch her forward and backward and forward and backward, each time cutting the wheel a little less, until her creaking chassis was parallel with the curb. Half an hour sped by, and she was still not completely parked. Sweat darkened my shirt under the arms, and I was thankful Papa Car had air conditioning. Amazingly, I had kept myself clean. Not even my white shoe and a half had picked up any dirt.

Just as Mama Car was close enough to the curb, I remembered that I had never checked the train schedule. I kept a piece of it in my wallet, but the weekend departures and arrivals were tacked up on the bulletin board in the kitchen.

I let myself back into the house and found the information I needed. It was 12:30. The next train left at 12:50. In the mornings I gave myself twenty-five minutes to make the trip, but I always had six or seven minutes to spare before the train actually pulled in.

I tacked the schedule up again and limped as fast as I could to the door. As soon as I closed it behind me, the phone rang. If I went back in to answer the phone, I'd surely miss the 12:50.

I hobbled out of the breezeway and got into Papa Car. The door was unlocked, all the windows were open. There was the faint smell of vomit, and I guessed that the windows had been left open to help air out the car. I rolled them all up and started the engine so I could turn on the air conditioner. I had shoved my white jacket to the passenger side of the seat. While the engine idled and the vents blew uncooled air, I reached over to straighten the jacket and noticed that a bright green lollipop was stuck to one lapel.

"Jesus shit," I muttered under my breath, trying to unstick the half-eaten lolly. Fred Astaire would just leave it there and people would fall in love with his "cute" carnation, I thought. But I was really pissed.

The lolly came off easily enough, but it left a spot. Forty minutes hauling a car out of the driveway by hand and I didn't get a single spot of dirt on my clothes. One second in the car and bam.

I released the emergency brake, put Papa into reverse, and stalled. I knew the air conditioner was an enormous drain, but I kept it on while I started Papa up again. This time the car shot out of the driveway without a hitch. A toy fire engine rolled the length of the rear windshield as I steered the car into the street. I had sixteen minutes.

Papa Car moved fast and handled easily. Too easily. For the first mile, until I got unused to the way Mama handled, I was overturning corners and stopping too short. But the feel came back to me, and by the time I reached the highway I was humming along like a teenager, weaving in and out of lanes, beating lights, passing on the left and right, anticipating the curves and bumps and potholes effortlessly. At the first overpass, I checked my watch and knew that I would make the train. Papa did fifty and sixty where Mama was lucky to climb to forty-five. And there was hardly any traffic.

Also, it was a different kind of traffic whenever a few cars did congest. The cars were bigger, newer, shinier. They carried at least one passenger, mostly two or three, children invariably among them, often a dog, too. Instead of sleepy-eyed, anxious, solitary businessmen at the wheel, the drivers were relaxed, cheerful, one elbow resting out the window; they were daddies, hubbies; they were glad they had to pay attention to the road rather than to their families;

they whistled or sang or finger-drummed along with the radio; they drove slowly, as if they did not care when they got where they were going, as if getting there were all the fun, and they stayed in their own lanes. It did not matter if the next lane opened up; they did not pull out and pass. Only I did that.

I cut off a station wagon in my haste to make it through an amber signal. When I checked his reaction in my rearview mirror, the driver looked more bewildered than angry, but his wife was yelling at him.

Would Mrs. P. do such a thing? I wondered, as I turned off the highway into a shortcut that would take me through the poorer section of town. I had never driven this section in the middle of Saturday, in the middle of any day. Usually these few blocks were deserted at seven-thirty in the morning and seven-thirty at night when I rattled to and from work holding my nose, my eyes, my breath against the squalor and spilled garbage and the sprinkling of sweating, possibly dangerous, deadbeats. But today everyone was home and in the street: dusty kids, drunken teenagers, scarred old men with protruding rib cages, fat women trying to coax a breeze up their discount dresses.

But the center of this doomed society was the Heaven on Earth Church of the Pentateuch. I had always assumed it was a fancy, tax-exempt front for a social club with folding craps tables under the pews, if there were pews, and a congregational supply of liquor up on the altar behind the colorfully cloaked holy paraphernalia.

As hurried as I was, I had to slow down and rubberneck when I pulled near the fight in front of the church. A bearded, T-shirted black man was screaming at a woman who could have been his wife or one of the girls in his stable. He called her every combination of filth he could come up with: a shit-sucking douche bag, a nigger-nookie dishrag, a bug ass cock-buster. The curses made almost no sense at all except that somehow they perfectly expressed the man's rage and hatred and disgust. The woman was on her knees, crying, trying to hug her assailant's grimy, too-big pant leg. The one thing she kept yelling between sobs was something about wine, too much of it, I guessed.

None of the ringside crowd noticed that I had come to a stop for no other reason than to join them in watching the spectacle.

They were too busy siding with the man; they had to be on his side, or wouldn't someone have stopped such an obviously unfair fight and comforted the poor woman, protected her, prevented her from turning the man's temper into physical abuse?

But the crowd seemed to be rooting the slowly boiling man on just by their unknightly lack of outrage.

Suddenly the man bent down and grabbed hold of the woman by the shoulder straps of her inappropriate evening gown. The scene appeared almost biblical; a tall, gaunt, bearded man with every possible outward sign of self-righteousness slowly lifted a scarlet-dressed harlot to her high-heeled feet, the brightly colored, hand-painted HEAVEN ON EARTH arching overhead like a rainbow or backdrop or Welcome Home sign or Renaissance inscription.

With one hand he held her at arm's length. With his right hand he punched her on the side of her jaw. Her head snapped back and her body went limp. Then he punched her again, a much fiercer blow to the temple.

His punches caused a sinking, fluttering cyclone of painless shock in my balls. I wanted to interfere, but I glanced at my watch and saw that I couldn't possibly make the 12:50 if I didn't pull away immediately. I kept the punching, cursing man in my rearview mirror for as long as I could as Papa Car picked up more and more speed. When I turned the next corner, the crowd, the man, the woman, the church, all slid beyond the mirror into the oblivion of their own reality.

In five minutes the train would wheeze into the station; no problem, I thought, as I steered into my regular parking lot and up the pebbly grade toward space number six. But another car was in my place.

I honked for the owner/attendant, a muscular foreigner who also owned the pub across the street. Instead, an elderly stumble-bum staggered out of the little shed, his fly open, his eyes wincing in the sunlight, his undershirt stained the color of human disease.

"Where's the guy who runs the lot?" I demanded impatiently.

"I'm here today," the stumblebum rasped, with more authority than I expected.

"Someone's in my place."

"No one's in yer place."

"That's my space, six. I pay by the month."

"I don't know nothin about that. Pull her over here and leave the key. It's two bucks."

"The reason I have six is because it's against the fence. I don't block anyone so I don't have to leave the key. Sometimes I get back very late, the lot's closed. And I already told you, I'm paid up for the month."

"I got orders. It's two bucks and you have to leave the key."

I had four minutes.

"Look, I'll give you your two bucks, but I'm not going to leave the key. Twelve's open, I'll pull in up there if you get that Chevy out of the way."

The old man just turned away and headed back to the shed as though he had had enough of me. I heard a snatch of baseball play-by-play soar out from behind the shed's ill-fitting door like the home run it was describing.

"Jesus shit," I yelled after the stumblebum.

At the entrance to the lot, between the shed and the curb, there was space for a single privileged car, usually the muscular young foreigner's racy red Corvette. But obviously he was not around, nor would he be if his hired hand was living in his shed, listening to his portable radio, and insulting his regular customers. I backed out of the drive and rolled into the owner's spot. Because of a telephone pole, I couldn't open the door very wide and had to squeeze out of the car slowly, awkwardly, babying my foot while holding on to my jacket as well. Three minutes, but still no sound of the train.

The stumblebum started to scream at me.

"I'll call the cops. I'll get Kenny Dugan down here. Kenny Dugan's my nephew. You can't park there, you sonofabitch."

When he mentioned his nephew, I pictured the curly-headed, freckly-faced second in command at Five-O, Dano, Danny, Kenny, and a shiver of unfathomable fear shimmied through me. The only thing to do was pay the old man. Overpay him.

"Look, here's five bucks. Keep the change."

"I don't want your money. It'll cost ya a damn sight more'n five when Kenny Dugan hauls your ass in. I'm gonna get this shit towed the hell outta here. You watch me if I don't."

But he didn't go to the phone. He started to stamp angrily all

around the lot, grumbling and cursing to himself and the cars, trying to decide, I decided, whether or not he really had a case against
me, and, if he did, whether the lot full of cars was secure enough for
him to leave for a minute to go across the street to make the call to
his nephew.

"I'm leaving the money in here," I called out to him. What else
could I do? I put the five on the shelf next to the radio and goose-
ran toward the station as fast as my foot and heel could carry me.

I was sorry I had exasperated the old man; he was only doing
his job. I was sorry that my total disregard for his momentary mission in life had made him feel ridiculous and unnecessary to the de-
gree that he had to let off steam way up there among the rows of
cars, out of my sight. But I was also vaguely concerned that he'd
do something stupid to reinstate his own integrity, like actually get
Papa Car towed away, or ticketed at least, or illegally unlocked,
jump-started, and then abandoned in front of Heaven on Earth for
it to be picked clean by a flock of black buzzards.

No time even to buy the papers. The train was pulling in.
I heard the screeching braking as I cursed the escalator for not
working and took the first of what, in my mind, amounted to a
thousand stairway steps.

The hydraulic release of air pressure opened the train doors and
gave me thirty seconds at the most to make it up to the platform
and into a car. No one else was on the stairway. No one else was
exiting the station house to board the train. Panic punched my
heart: what if the train pulled away without me? The trainmen sel-
dom waited one second longer than necessary to stick to their
schedules; at least once a week some huffing, puffing commuter was
left helplessly behind, wreathed in the melodramatic sound of gust-
ing white railway steam; what if I were the one today?

With my keys and my jacket still in one hand I rushed out of
the station house, hobbled to a halt, and called out to the nearest
trainman to wait for me. When he spotted my foot, he stopped folding up the little stairway between cars and yelled some yardbird
code word down the line.

Thanking him for waiting, I pulled myself up and caught my
breath as the train rolled out.

The smoking car was three forward, and my foot and the motion of the train made me reel down the aisle. At one track switch I fell into a seat, but the car was empty except for three people who were sitting ahead of where I fell, so no one noticed. I decided to sit there and compose myself until I had to have a cigarette.

I took a deep breath and remembered that I had forgotten my eyeglasses. Immediately I pictured them on the redwood railing of the swimming pool deck. I didn't really need them, only at twilight and when I was driving, or to sharpen movies or sporting events or stage shows. If I put them on, I tended to get used to them and wore them for the next few hours until my ears and the bridge of my nose became sore. But my ears and nose were not sore. Most likely I hadn't worn the glasses today even though I had been down by the pool; I probably had taken them off another time and put them on the railing, the night before perhaps. I couldn't remember, it was as if the missing glasses were blurring my memory.

It was easier to look ahead, to plot and stage the afternoon's entertainment. I felt that I was about to go on a blind date, except only she was blind; I already knew what she looked like, how she carried herself, what she thought about very private subjects, how she spoke. I knew secrets her own husband hadn't heard.

I felt as high as a high school football hero coming off a five-touchdown game; the season is over, the next big event is the prom. That was it. I felt as if I were picking up my prom date. Quite possibly I had even unconsciously dressed for the occasion.

Not since I was a teenager had I felt anything like my present anticipation. The prom, my real prom, when I had escorted my wife-to-be to the local country club and then to the Copacabana, had by its own nature made a man of me. I wore a white dinner jacket. Custom dictated that I present my date with a wrist corsage, that I pick her up in a polished car, that I grease the palm of the maitre d' at the most glamorous night club of them all. As a purely ritualistic function of high school graduation, the entire bright lights night had celebrated my turning from someone who had led a school life because the law said so into someone who was at last ready to make his own voluntary way in the world. This afternoon I would turn once again into a man who made his own way. But for the time being, until Les Brown and his Band of Renown struck up "The Party's Over," the way was as fated as a prom night. I would wear my most dashing outfit; I would present Mrs. P. with an irresistible seduction, one that caressed her wrist and led her to my office, and then I would spend all of my worldly experience on her, dazzle her with a thousand crisscrossing spotlights, all focused on me.

I kicked the backrest of the seat in front of me forward with my good foot so I could rest the bad one on the seat. Sometimes the trainman ordered feet off the seats, but I hoped he'd understand today.

Suddenly the train jerked to a halt. The company had been repairing tracks, and when the train made a station stop, the engineer had to try to line up the doors with the bright yellow planks that had been laid on the torn-up tracks to help the passengers on and off. Occasionally he saw that he might overshoot the planks and slammed on the brakes, figuring one quick jostle was better than a difficult climb up or down the gangway steps.

What amazed me was how long I had been sitting and musing without itching for a cigarette; the train made two equally spaced stops en route, so I had gone a third of the way. The day was speeding. Mrs. P. was getting closer and closer.

Suddenly I heard uproarious crowd noise. Then they poured into the train, a hundred of them, more, dressed like gypsies, unkempt as hobos, unruly and boisterous as passionate rioters, pushing each other out of the way, diving into seats, smoking, yelling, gurgling their obnoxious teenage giggle, fighting over who got to sit next to the window, who got to sit next to the beer, who got to sit next to the girl with the biggest tits, who didn't get to sit next to me. They actually sniffed and stole glances at me as if I were the one who needed a shave and a haircut and a good scrubbing and clothing that was neatly pressed and decently matched.

Three of the horde lost at musical chairs and had no other choice but to squeeze into my foursome of seats; I had no other choice but to remove my foot and let them.

One plopped into the aisle seat next to me before I could snatch my jacket out of his way.

"Watch it," I ordered him, immediately sorry I had taken such a nasty tone. The onslaught of teenagers probably meant there were no other seats in the train, certainly not in the smoking car which they always filled first and where they were so brave as to pass joints on the way to and from rock concerts; I couldn't change my seat, and I couldn't stand the rest of the way because of my foot, and I couldn't bury myself in a newspaper.

"This your coat?" the kid said innocently, and I was glad he gave me the chance to offer a hollow but apologetic "It's all right."

If we were going to be on top of one another for the rest of the ride, our knees banging into each other's every time the car jerked or swerved or one of us got restless, if I had to listen in on their conversation whether or not any of us wanted me to, at least we could start off on semirelaxed terms. I knew from experience that these kids could be tough on someone they mistrusted or thought mistrusted them.

Of course, I did have one recourse. I could disappear. No one in my field had a better reputation for disappearing than I when I was a moderator. I could sit down in a room full of squeamish housewives or red-necked blue-collar workers, ask them awkward, personal, embarrassing, provocative, never-been-raised questions, and then melt into the woodwork while they jabbered on and on in what they felt was the privacy of their own class. I never intruded my possibly superior, certainly different, self. Even as I manipulated them, as I turned some against others, crowned or deposed leaders, reinforced the shy ones, deflated the liars, even then I was the unseen puppeteer, the man who was not important on the stage.

Maybe it was the way I looked—nondescript—or acted—wide-eyed and nonaggressive—or talked—more like a student than a teacher—or maybe it was a combination of all these traits, but my fellow moderators had to hand it to me. More than one stole a bit of me and incorporated it into his or her performance before the one-way mirror.

It would be tougher in the train and in my getup (which was all the more outrageous in comparison), but if worst came to worst, I could try to summon up that old talent. I could try to disappear.

But first, why not test the water? During a long and close-quartered train ride, strangers might get to know one another despite themselves. After all, hadn't I just been feeling mighty like a teenager? Wasn't I the ageless Mr. Fred Astaire, everybody's dancing partner, everybody's lover or brother or uncle or pal?

The one who had accidentally pressed my white sport jacket (and then made me wear it by taking its seat) was quickly identified by his friends as Stu, or Stewie, or Stupe, or El Stupido, depending on how they felt from moment to moment. He was my height and possibly handsome, if only someone put a scissors and comb to his ragmop hair. Without obviously staring at him, I could watch his hands and legs. His hands picked at one another nervously; his bouncing legs kept constant, rapid time to a song only he could hear.

Across from us were Red (who didn't have red hair) and Chicorski (who was one of those kids everyone always affectionately calls by his surname, not in the manner of a drill instructor, that would come later). The two of them looked like they came from different planets; Red was short and chubby and his features tended to disintegrate in the overall fleshiness of his face, while Chicorski was tall, well built, and, at first, second, and third glances, all features. His nose drooped a long way down to his toothy mouth. His ears peeked through his silken blond pageboy. His eyes were magnified by thick, rimless spectacles and accented by two very high arching brows that caterpillared all over his forehead when he spoke. And when he spoke, when any one of them spoke, of course it was on the subject of sex. It seemed to me, as I took a disguised look all around the car, that teenagers were always a moment away from coming. If you touched them in the right place, they would. The car seemed bathed in a pink pubescent glow. If the seven ages of man were metaphorically depicted as the rise and fall of the male member, the teenage years would certainly represent the hardest of hard-ons, the diaphanous droplet or two before spurting young adulthood.

"You never fucked shit," was Chicorski's answer to whatever Stu had claimed. "Me and Red was there that whole night, and we talked to her, too, and she woulda tole us."

"Bullshit. She ain't gonna say nothin' to you guys," said Stupe, as I was sure they were about to call him. But they didn't. They let it pass.

"Anyway, Chicorski made it three times that night, didn't you, Chicorski?" bragged Red, encouraging the biggest, toothiest grin I ever saw to tell it again.

"Hey, Stewie," Chicorski began in a low whisper, "you never

done it, right? Ya still pound it, right? Let me tell you, I had my hand right up there, Stewie. This hand. Here, ya wanna smell it?" and he threw three fingers into Stewie's nose before Stewie could duck out of the way. Then Red and the big grin laughed like The Great Gildersleeve and playfully grabbed at each other's balls.

The three of them were obvious friends, yet the twosome across from us ganged up on Stewie again and again on the subject of sexual experience; sometimes in a mean-spirited, joking way which wasn't so bad, but other times in a serious, almost sensitive manner that must have crushed my fidgety partner.

"Hey, seriously, Stupe, me and Red are gonna get you laid before school starts, man. But we can only do so much; I mean we'll set it up, but you gotta make it on yer own when the time comes."

"You like Amy, doncha?" propositioned Red. "You always liked Amy, everybody knows that. C'mon, El Stupido, whataya shruggin' yer fuckin' shoulders for, you like Amy, big deal. Shit, Stupe, I'm tellin' ya Amy'll go down for you. Kauffman had his hand on her bare ass at a rock concert—Kauffman! I'll bet there ain't a fuckin' girl in North Plainfield who don't do somethin'. Djoo know that Mick got a blow job in the fuckin' movies last week? I ain't tellin' ya who 'cause I tole Mick I wouldn't. But right there in the middle of *Star Wars*."

"May the force be with you," Chicorski chimed in, and once more that awful teenage howling shattered the noisy car.

Leave him alone, I wanted to say. If it were me I'd have been ready to explode. I'd have blown the head right off my dick and drowned my tormentors in wet dreams.

The trainman forced the heavy door open and entered the car to punch everyone's ticket. When he saw the thick smoke he bellowed a warning, but twenty different voices immediately objected.

"What the hell, everyone's smoking, make it a smoking car."

"This is America, ain't it? Majority rules."

"Give us a break, huh?"

"Whadya gonna do, throw us off?"

"We're the only ones on this goddamn train."

"Fancy pants don't mind," Chicorski yelled out, and I realized he was referring to me.

The trainman threw up his hands like a weary mother and slid the panel over the No in the No Smoking sign above the entrance to our car. The passengers gave him a whistling, foot-stomping round of applause, while I myself took advantage of the liberal Saturday shift by lighting up a cigarette.

"Listen, Stewie, we'll go down to McArthur Street tonight and round up a bimbo for you." Red was anxious to get back to Stewie's initiation. "Ya ever done it with a whore, Stu?"

"That's good, Stupe, a whore's a good idea," Chicorski agreed, " 'cause she'll show ya how and make sure yer doin' it right. That's her job, man."

In all this time, through all this instinctive sarcasm and transparent boasting, Stu said nothing. Maybe his friends were right about him. Or maybe he was afraid he'd make a bigger fool of himself. Maybe he was afraid he'd cry if he struck back at them.

"The trick," Red lowered his voice and raised an eyebrow to dramatize his imminent words of wisdom, "is to get it good and wet so it don't rub. The real trick is to get her to get it wet."

He could not stand it one second longer. He felt enclosed. He felt unborn. Only a drastic gesture or outcry could get him through.

"Any of you boys ever tit-fucked?" I was as surprised as they were to hear from me.

"Tit-fucked," I repeated, feigning amazement at their blank expressions. I should have stopped right there.

But, "It's a very good position," I went on, "when you're . . . not yourself. For example if you've just drunk a pint of vodka."

The three of them were staring at me, a little afraid of me.

"Of course, you probably do it all the time, Red. You, too, Chicorski. Me, I was quite a bit older than you fellows when I got around to the study of sexual positions. There are hundreds of them, I'm sure you're aware, but not all of them suit everyone alike. Tit-fucking just happens to suit us all, though, doesn't it? I found that out, well, let me see, I guess when I was in college, or about to enter college, anyway. It was one of those unbelievably beautiful nights that only nature can get away with; purple and blue and black and bright yellow—if a painter ever did that he'd never have a chance. Not even Van Gogh. Not even Chagall. And we were on the bank of a lake, too, beneath a full moon. You can't even put that sort of thing in a popular song anymore."

I was looking out the window as I spoke. Great heaps of garbage whizzed by.

"I had had my eye on this particular girl all day. She was beautiful. And I was irresistible in my uniform. I asked her to meet me by the lake at midnight, which she did. Even in the blackness her soft brown eyes hypnotized me. Her face glowed in the moonlight. I remember thinking she was an angel that had just fallen out of the sky. I told her . . ." Gulls hovered over the mountains of garbage. "I said to her . . ." Suddenly I snapped out of it and turned flamboyantly toward the teenagers. "Well, I laid trusty dick right up between her heavenly heavin' tits and squooshed them tight around me and did a layin' down jig, me boys. Squoosh. Squoosh. And then the bulwark broke and the flood poured outta me all down her lovely neck and shoulders and she never knew what hit her, lads. Never guessed. Never asked. And as for me, well, I love 'em and leave 'em, don't you?"

Where were they? Oh, they were there, but they had disappeared. I was the one who was supposed to. But they were the ones who did.

•

The E train was empty, and I felt like an early-morning derelict. My hands were dirty. My jacket was soiled and wrinkled. My shoe had begun to unravel a bit, and I was afraid that if I tried to pull off the trailing stitches the whole damned thing would come apart. I must have looked like the morning after. Being alone made me feel deserted. But I satisfied myself that it was lunchtime and that was why the sluggish subway was so desolate. I pictured the engineer with one hand on a chicken salad sandwich, the other sleepily working the throttle.

Even though the ride was to be short, I was tempted to let myself fall asleep. The only other passenger, a stylishly dressed woman in her middle ages, was standing even though every seat but mine was unoccupied. Her energy kept me guiltily awake.

The woman, who was reading a book, never acknowledged the public address announcement which statically, almost unintelligibly, informed us about the delay. As soon as possible our train would be given clearance; until such time would we please be patient. Years of transcribing overlapping, indistinct voices from tape recordings had enabled me to figure out every word of the message. The woman merely turned a page, shifted her weight, and realized that she no longer had to hold onto the overhead bar to steady herself.

Although it was the perfect setting for Fred Astaire to pirouette over and strike up an instantly theatrical relationship, whatever had been getting me down was growing stronger.

I slapped my thigh to keep awake. I tried to read the title of the woman's book from a car's length away and from between her dainty fingers and without my glasses. I read the backlit ads for life insurance, chewing gum, secretarial school, a restaurant decorated like a ship's galley, another thing to do with aluminum foil, the only thing to do about retirement.

And then I came to the photo and bio of the current Miss Subways.

> Evelyn Pfeiffer . . . 18 years old.
> Part time student at F.I.T.
> Currently a secretary at the
> law firm of Scott and Associates.
> Loves horseback riding, tennis,
> swimming . . . hobbies include
> amateur photography. Hopes to be
> a fashion designer or interior
> decorator.

The resemblance was uncanny. The same eyes, mouth, coloring, the same spunky expression that must have once inhabited the now resigned face of Mrs. P.

Pfeiffer had to be a pseudonym, of course, and a perfect one at that. What an absolute stroke of genius to pay silent homage to her mother with that ghostly initial P and at the same time ward off telephone-booth breathers, subway mashers, back-alley rapists, Central Park muggers, schoolyard molesters.

I stood up and limped across the aisle for a closer look at the photo. There were tiny squares of the photographer's light forever in Evelyn's eyes. And still my own were dull and delirious with sleep. I held onto a pole to keep from crumpling to the floor and sensed my fellow passenger's calm but poised wariness. Despite my excitement over this preliminary chance meeting with Mrs. P., I felt drained and lifeless.

And then, with no announcement, the car jerked to life. The lights flickered and the floor vibrated. The lights went out, and I looked at the end doors to see if our car was the only one. To my left, past the shadow of the woman, the next car was black. To my right it was black too, but the darkness was punctured by blinking red lights, and I realized, I remembered, I was in the lead car. But the lights were receding. The train was going backwards. Slowly, slowly, it pulled back out of the tunnel, a track tie at a time, it seemed. I had never heard of a subway that went in reverse. I'd only heard of trains stuck between stations and riders having to squeeze out and press themselves against the primeval wall to breathlessly inch their way back to the light.

I held my breath as my eyes grew accustomed to the streaky red darkness. I clung to the pole and felt myself slipping as slowly, but as surely, as the movement of the train.

There were two women with me who were mocking my steady fall: the woman with the book who might still be reading for all her unflappable uprighteousness. And Miss Subways, lovely Evelyn, those damned squares of light still gleaming in the dark like cat's eyes. I imagined her poster fluttering off the wall and swooping down on me like an avenging pterodactyl. Oh, that silent P. Was I going mad? Was I drifting away? Not into sleep, but into twilight? Where were my glasses? I needed them at twilight.

The train made awful, grating sounds as if it were traveling against the grain of the tunnel. The winged poster of the youthful Mrs. P. flapped and batted about my ears. In the distance I heard the impossibly loud sounds of pages turning and an impatient foot tapping. The grating and flapping and batting and turning and tapping became louder and louder, drowning out the wild thumping of my heart and the roaring silence of my held breath. They were growing stronger as I grew weaker. One's eyes glowed in the black car, the other one's could read in the dark. And mine still struggled to close. A heaviness was still upon me. My hands burned as they stuttered down the steel pole.

And then . . . and then . . . the light. The light at the beginning of the tunnel. The light of the previous station filtered through the disintegrating darkness.

The train stopped. The doors hissed open. The woman tucked her book under her arm and strode out onto the empty platform. The poster was still up in its frame, the eyes a bit dimmer now because the rear lighting was still off.

And I breathed. I breathed. And the breath made a noise you hear only in the middle of the night.

•

All my life I had seen leaden, virtually unconscious men sleep-walk through the contrastingly animated streets of New York City. Once, when I was young, I stopped one of them and we talked for an hour about his wife and daughter who were living in Baltymore, neither of whom he had laid his bloodied, glimmerless eyes on in more than twenty years.

"Was I so wrong?" he'd asked me after cataloging each of his "misunderstood" attempts to come to grips with his past life.

"I couldn't work for a guy like that—was I so wrong?"

Or, "What can I tell ya, the bottle always came first. One time I was off it but then I got this here cancer of the jaw, see the hole here? and the doc tells me if the pain gets too bad take a little nip. What would you do? Was I so wrong?"

Or, "She was an old, old friend, you know what I mean, and she was feelin' sorry for herself, and I was feelin' pretty good, as a matter of fact, and she invites me up to look at this picture, see, of her husband who was just kilt over there in that Korea, and, well, one thing kinda led to another, and you know what I was doin'? You know what I was really doin'? I was just tryin' to make her stop cryin'. Now tell me, was I so wrong?"

Vernon Aloysius Hoshkins his name was. Maybe we'd bump into one another today. Maybe we wouldn't even look up if we did.

All my life I'd seen them walk close to the buildings, and now I was one of them. Even though I had a purpose, a place to go, a fine woman to seduce, my heart was no longer in it. There was still unfinished business with Mrs. P. that got me up and out of the premature station stop and into the crowded streets and moving in the vague direction of my office, but I wasn't a graceful Fred

Astaire skipping up and down the curb, ad-libbing dance steps on a stoop, running up the side of a building, leapfrogging hydrants and trash baskets, hitching a little ride on the back bumper of a bus suddenly alive with a syncopated cast of singers and dancers disguised as ordinary passengers.

No, I was Vernon Aloysius Hoshkins, slowly and aimlessly making my way back to Baltymore. But first I better sleep in this park, first I better wet my whistle, first I better hit on that fine-looking kid for a smoke or a *quewter* or a bit of friendly chitchat just to pass the time. Am I so wrong?

It was amazing how filthy bare toes could get in a single city block. Equally amazing was how people hotfooted it out of the way to give a wide berth to anyone whose toes were exposed.

Yet despite my mood, my pilot light was not completely out. It flickered, it was dim, but still that tiny flame of anticipation warmed the general vicinity of my loins. The last image of Evelyn Pfeiffer kept creeping into the face of every woman on the street. It seemed, in fact, that I was the only man in the city. Everywhere I looked there were women of all ages, all colors, all shapes. I felt an unexaggerated flood of tenderness for each one I saw. I wanted to touch them, hug them, kiss away the tears which once had been little squares of reflected light.

What I really wanted was to be stark naked among them. I wanted the one with the swollen shopping bag to spread her gifts at my feet, tear off her clothes, and impale her sex on my filthy big toe. I wanted the fat lady to lift me onto her head as if I were her two-year-old and bury her face in my freshly talc'd balls. I didn't know what I wanted.

On the one hand, my heart leaped out to these women and I yearned to mother them, or son them, and somehow let them know that I did care about their frilly clothes and frilly thoughts and pat, teased, lacquered existences. But a moment later I wanted to make them crawl and salivate and pay for their own culpability. I wanted to punch them, yes, and call them every dirty word I could think of. And through it all, whether my mood rose or fell, I wanted Mrs. P.

All of them merged into her: the fat lady and the shopping bag lady and the mother with stroller and the mother with teenage daughter and the two wispy-waspy high fashion models and the lady from uptown, the lady from downtown, the lady from Cleveland, the lady from Spain, the so-very-much-in-love fiancée, the so-very-tired grandmother, the gay divorcée, the blind woman with the agonized smile and silent tambourine, the chauffeur-driven dowager, the theater party from Hadassah, the doll with the itsy-bitsy nose and owlish sunglasses, the eternal cheerleader bob-bob-bobbing along, the middle-management token female who felt she had to work Saturdays to earn less than her strictly nine-to-five male counterparts, the housewife on her day off, the hooker on her day on, the waitress on her lunch break, the art student busily sketching the photographer busily snapping the aspiring violinist busily serenading the Hare Krishna busily converting the nun in her summer habit, the overweight adolescent spilling out of a jogging suit, the gum-cracking hoyden shoving two fingers into a marbelized bowling ball, the saleslady blinding me with her diamond ring as she recorded the vital information of my purchase onto the Master Charge form and cranked it through the machine.

"One minute, please," she cheerfully informed me. "The computer has to okay you."

"Of course it does." I smiled, wondering what a nice, well-fed, brilliantly jeweled, professionally coiffed, carefully dressed, obviously married, probably multiparous Long Islander like her was doing in a place like this, selling me a complete set of children's golf clubs, with bag, with tax, expensive; and what I was doing buying it.

"Don't bother wrapping it," I said, when the computer allowed me to leave. "In fact," I had a better idea, "why don't I just take these clubs out of the box and put them in the bag . . . ," I explained what I wanted while I was doing it, "and then I can just sling the whole thing on my shoulder like this," I said, slinging, "and play through," I said, hauling the three-quarter-sized clubs out the door.

Once I saw a man driving a motorized chair along the sidewalk in front of St. Patrick's Cathedral; there's that Central Park inhabitant who painted himself purple every morning; another time up on Madison Avenue, it was a Saturday afternoon in fact, my wife and I saw a man walking briskly toward us in nothing but gym shorts, and then when he passed, we saw that he had emptied his bowels in his pants, down the backs of his well-muscled legs—right in front of the Frick Museum, too; there are clowns and transvestites and guys in ape suits and women dressed like broccoli to plug health food restaurants and jugglers and forty-year-old ten-year-olds who have just skateboarded across America and millionaires and movie stars—so why would anyone think it at all extraordinary to see me goose-hobbling up the Fifth Avenue fairway with a bag of sawed-off golf clubs slung over the crimped shoulder of my white sport jacket?

No one did. Least of all me. Moments ago the streets were teeming with female life. Now they seemed empty, still, untrafficked. Occasionally there was a sign that someone had been this way before: a smoking cigarette butt, an asphalt divot, a wad of gum big as a liquid center golf ball. But if I concentrated, I could see through the iron knolls and the blinking branches and the far off foursome of blue-shirted building attendants taking dead aim with their mops at a speck of dirt on the tiled floor of the lobby; I could see ahead and over and in and right up to the cup of hot coffee on my desktop.

My legs were so heavy. I felt as if I were sunk into the sidewalk up to my knees. I was panting. I was sweating through my shirt and the seat of my pants. My vision limped with my feet, bouncing objects into the air and then flinging them down again. At one point I had to drop the bag from my shoulder and drag it along behind me by its padded strap. It bounced, and the club shafts rattled against one another and made me think of a tin can tail on a bridegroom's flivver.

But it was still early. If only I could contain my enthusiasm—what I meant was if only I could *maintain* my enthusiasm—there was still time to wash up, straighten my clothing, have that hot cup of coffee, lay down the Astaire Studio dance prints, and then, then, after pulling myself and everything else together, call Mrs. P.

•

No matter how often I worked late or came in on the weekend, I never got used to being in my office when it was empty. There were only four other people on staff, but I kept straining to hear a typewriter, or the Xerox machine, or the gurgle of the water cooler,

or Mad Minnie, as we called the feverishly high-pitched sound of a
rewinding tape recording. No one knew for sure what Minnie
Mouse sounded like, but once, when my older boy was my only
boy, he heard that squeaky, backward voice and asked if it were
Minnie Mouse (Minnie, not Mickey, of course) and why did she
sound so crazy; and, with an adult touch of alliterative refinement,
the name stuck.

Today, however, the very things that usually made me uneasy
about my empty office seemed to work to my advantage.

It was like being in school after all the teachers had gone home.
There was a flickering feeling of wrongdoing, of mischievousness.
And it was suspenseful, too; someone might bust in while you were
going through your teacher's drawers or prowling around the principal's office. And strangely enough, I seemed to represent the
violated, unwitting figure of authority. I felt as if I were spying on
myself—my other, surefooted, business-as-usual, unremarkably at-
tired self.

When I flicked on the light, I looked around to see if my other
self was in the room. When I pulled open the file cabinet, I listened
for my own footsteps in the corridor.

A. A. A. A. B. Ballantine Beer . . . Ben-Gay . . . Benson &
Hedges . . . B. F. Goodrich (wrong, should be under G) . . . Bic
Lighters . . . Bickford's Coffee Shop . . . Big Boy Shops (what
was that? the elevator?) . . . Bisodol (passed it) . . . Bickford's . . . Birth Control!

When I pulled out the folder, my anxiety intensified. I took it to
my desk, sat down, and turned to the typewritten transcript of
Mrs. P. and her fellow group members' prompted, seduced, provoked, extracted, abreactional secret thoughts about femininity,
masculinity, marriage, cohabitation, intercourse, pregnancy, birth,
life, death, religion, existence, everything. It was like being there all
over again in the smoke-filled, high-voltage atmosphere of the conference room. The members were edgy, uncomfortable; they re-
gretted having agreed to open up about themselves for a measly
twelve dollars, a few cups of coffee, and one or two quick-drying
triangles of white meat turkey on rye. More than a few cups of
coffee, actually. That session held the record—three pots. Big pots.
And they could have drunk more.

In making my report, I had underlined in red all the important statements I had wanted to pull out of the transcript and include, and that saved me the trouble now of finding the highlights.

The breakthrough comment, the one that finally broke the icy reluctance to say things that had never been uttered before—and utter them to virtual strangers—was made by Mrs. Marino, a devout Catholic who hated society's increasing disregard for her unquestioning faith.

MRS. M.: If I did decide to use a birth control device, and I never would, but if I did, I would not talk about it with my husband. No. There are some things . . .

Mrs. Terhune, an emaciated Irish Catholic with eight children, interrupted. She had been waiting for just the right moment, waiting her whole life to unburden herself. I could almost see her racing down the church aisle and flinging herself into the confessional.

MRS. T.: That's right. You said it. You can't talk to a man about a thing like that. A man doesn't want to know these things. You can't. I've seen it in my own life. Listen, I've got eight kids, and, believe me, four were enough. But it's not for me to deny my husband or God. There were plenty of times when I wanted to, but you can't. How can you?

By then she was looking for any member to speak up, or nod, or in some way indicate to her that she understood what Mrs. T. was saying and that Mrs. T. was right. And they all did. The tape reel might have spun off the deck from so many, such impassioned, such sudden outpourings of release. It was at this point that the transcript suddenly looked like the manuscript of a fifty-character drama. They all wanted to talk at once. Each one had another dark secret she wanted to get rid of. They kept interrupting each other; they leaped from topic to topic; they delivered knowing asides; they shouted their own versions of "Amen" after someone made a point that touched home. The members loosened up physically, too. Some got up out of their chairs and walked to the coffee urn, or to the other end of the table for another sandwich, or up to my easel for a closer look at the agency's rough renderings of what the birth control device in question might look like. Even if they didn't actually get out of their chairs, they made themselves more comfortable, allowed their bodies to slump into more accustomed positions, began playing with their hair, twirling a curl around a finger, for example; they took off earrings that might have pinched; they did not bother to fix smudged or faded lipstick; they permitted a stray bra strap to stay in sight.

MRS. R.: I watched my father try to ruin my mother's life with drinking and womanizing, and he'd stagger in and beat her every time. But could he break mama's spirit? Never. She adored that man.

MRS. K.: I was just like all the girls, anxious to get married, worried that if I threw away a good chance maybe I wouldn't ever get another one. [*Pause for knowing laughter*] So we got married when I was seventeen. What does a seventeen-year-old girl know about the world?

My eyes, my mind, darted through the transcript helter-skelter; I did not have to read the remarks in order, only recapture the mood, the excitement, the release, the sadness, the terrible resignation of this hopeless, dreamless, loyal, oh so loyal, species. (Did I feel the same way then?)

MRS. A.: I really don't know what to do. I know my daughter is going to be tempted. She's fifteen and she does go out with boys. Different boys, not just one. But she's not stupid; she knows what's going on; she's a bright girl; she's in the top of her class with grades, so she knows what's happening. Especially these days with all the sex on television. There was that show about a boy who gets a girl in trouble . . .

MRS. R.: I saw that show.

MRS. A.: . . . and he's a good boy. That's the point. I mean, my daughter might be tempted. I've taught her to be a good girl, but you know what they say, the flesh is weak. So what do I do; do I tell her about birth control and take her to a doctor for something? Or what? It's a real problem.

MRS. K.: I saw that show, too. She's right. It's a terrible problem these days.

MRS. B.: What night was it on? If it was on opposite "The Six-Million Dollar Man," I didn't get to see it. My ten-year-old has a fit if he misses "The Six-Million Dollar Man."

MRS. S.: How does this thing feel?

MODERATOR: You insert it yourself and for the first two or three days there may be very, very slight discomfort, something like a very mild menstrual cramp. But then you don't even know it's there.

MRS. S.: No, I mean how does it feel for my husband? Will he . . . when we . . . is there . . . ?

I came to the series of comments and observations and confessions that led up to Mrs. P.'s memorable remark. At first she was determined not to say a word, as though she were protecting every group member's deepest, darkest secret. At most she nodded shyly when one of the other wives plucked at her heartstrings. At last she spoke.

MRS. P.: My husband is used to his life. If I made a change, he'd notice.

MODERATOR: What do you mean? Give me an example.

I could tell she was sorry she had spoken. A few sentences later the source of her regret was apparent; it was her husband. Just speaking words out loud without his being nearby (in "his" chair, no doubt) to approve or disapprove or make a face that told her to shut up made her skittish.

MRS. P.: Well, one time when I used margarine instead of butter, he knew right away. As soon as he took a bite he made a funny face with his mouth and asked me what was different. And this wasn't a piece of bread and butter I'm talking about. This was a seven-layer cake. So you see how sensitive he is. Do you think I could start fooling around with birth control without him knowing?

MODERATOR: You could tell him.

MRS. P.: You don't know my husband. He's very set in his ways. If I told him I was going to use birth control, it would kill him.

MRS. M.: It would kill the baby.

MODERATOR: What would he do?

MRS. P.: I'm not sure he'd do anything. But he would be very upset.

MODERATOR: Doesn't it upset *you* that you have less control over your body and your life by not using birth control?

MRS. P.: I never thought about it. Sometimes thinking too much gets you nowhere but into trouble.

That had sounded like an old family saying. I could picture Mrs. P.'s father reprimanding her when she was a little girl for having played doctor or for having put on mommy's makeup; the old man towered over his trembling little girl and waited for her to say something in her defense.

"But I thought . . ." she would say, her little brain clickety-clacking like mad as she collected her reasons, good reasons to her. And then daddy would stop her with the one injunction that was to stick better than any of his others.

"You thought, you thought," he'd say until he, too, trembled. But it would be a different kind of trembling. "Thinking too much gets you nowhere but into trouble, young lady. You remember that. Now get up to your room and go to sleep. No dinner tonight for bad little girls who think too much."

MODERATOR: But you're not afraid your husband would reprimand you?

It was oh so fucking easy for a moderator to slip in and out of someone else's life.

MRS. P.: I just don't want him to be upset. Especially . . .

MODERATOR: Especially what?

I think it was then that I first noticed her jacket. The light got caught in the silver and turned gray and murky as she squirmed in her black vinyl chair.

MRS. P.: Especially then. You know.

She swiveled in her chair without moving her feet. A nervous swivel. And tapped her fingers on the unreflective vinyl arm.

MODERATOR: You think that knowing you had a birth control device would put a strain of some kind on sexual intercourse?

MRS. P.: That's a very personal area.

Why? Why, she kept asking herself, did I have to get myself into this? Why wasn't I a big girl? Too much thinking.

MODERATOR: For whom? You or your husband?

MRS. P.: Both of us.

A moment's peace. An answer that might put an end to this interrogation. But it didn't.

MODERATOR: So you would feel better without a birth control device?

MRS. P.:   I would feel better knowing my husband would feel better.

The art director sitting in blackness with me had said, "Now there's a woman after me own heart." The female account exec simply stared straight ahead in overacted disbelief.

MODERATOR: But wouldn't you like to feel more comfortable? I only say this because you didn't raise your hand when I asked who was opposed to birth control on moral or religious grounds. You're only opposed because in some way you think a birth control device would displease your husband. And I'm asking, what about you? Wouldn't you like to be pleased for a change?

MRS. P.:   I am pleased. If he is.

The moderator sensed Mrs. P.'s uneasiness and, fearing it would become contagious, sought to lighten the mood with a disastrous quip.

MODERATOR: Well, I hope your marriage is a little more democratic when it comes to orgasm.

Twelve cases of whiplash; every woman snapped to horrified attention. The moderator had allowed himself to exist, to appear, to be present in the room.

MRS. P.:   Women don't have orgasms. They just satisfy their husbands.

I inserted the tip of my suddenly stiff finger into the P hole.

They just satisfy their husbands. They just satisfy their husbands. They just work up a lather. They just dance to the whip. They just smile and swoon and moan on cue. They just swallow their husbands' pride. Oh yes, and when they make a mistake which might endanger the species, when pregnancy is untimely or ungainly or—uh oh—unwarranted, then they just go off in a corner and abort. And they lie about where they've been. The answer is not as simple as being kept barefoot and pregnant. The answer is that they must keep themselves very much alive and ripe and up to snuff . . . or else.

"God damn you, Mrs. P.," I said out loud, not believing my good fortune to know her, dialing the rest of her telephone number with the stiff tip of my finger; God damn you, Mrs. P.! How could anyone else have put it so . . . so honestly: they just satisfy their husbands.

"Hello?"

"Is this Mrs. Palaeo?"

"Yes, it is. Who's this?"

"Mrs. Palaeo, I'm calling about a focus group interview you took part in several years ago. It was on the subject of a new birth control device. You came up to my offices on Madison Avenue. Do you remember?"

"That was a long time ago. I do remember."

"The reason I'm calling, Mrs. Palaeo, is that I would like you to come up to those same offices today, this afternoon, in fact; there are a few follow-up questions I need to ask you."

"Today?"

"Yes. This afternoon, Mrs. Palaeo."

"But that birth control thing must have been five years ago."

"Three."

"I really can't come today. My husband will be home at four and . . ."

"I'm sure your husband would want you to come, Mrs. Palaeo."

"Who am I talking to?"

"You do want to satisfy your husband, don't you?"

"I'm sorry . . ."

"Mrs. Palaeo, before you hang up on me, does your husband know that you never reach a climax?"

She hung up.

I dialed again.

I counted ten rings before she answered.

"Mrs. Palaeo, does your husband know you had an abortion?"

"Please tell me what you want."

"I want you to come to my office. Today. Now. As soon as you hang up the phone, powder your nose and leave your husband a note. Tell him your mother's ill again. You had to run over and help out. Tell him the car broke down, you had to take it to the garage. I don't care what you tell him, Mrs. P. But if you don't tell him a lie, I'm going to have to tell him the truth about you, Mrs. P. The abortion, the playacting in bed, the margarine in the seven-layer cake. The truth, Mrs. P. Dog honest."

She will come. Of course she will come. There is no agonizing. No wheedling. She will come because it is part of her definition to come; if she doesn't, it is dangerous. The point of her whole life would shatter like an arrowhead against—

"Did you hear something?"

"No."

"I thought I heard a click."

"No."

"Do you have an extension, Mrs. Palaeo?"

"I didn't hear anything."

She will be here in an hour and a half.

•

It has been five years since I last moderated a focus group interview. Now I design the interview. I develop the objectives. I structure the questionnaire. I monitor the input and output. I sit behind the one-way mirror with my clients and reassure them, occasionally sending notes in to the moderator to help him get back on track or to find out something on the spur of the moment that may be helpful later. Finally I analyze the results and make my report.

When I begin a session, the conference room has already been set up by the moderator, who is in charge of any recording equipment the members are allowed to see, and by the client, who provides samples of the concept, or the advertising, or of the product itself in its finished or hypothetical form. My secretary simply buzzes me when the members arrive. I like to watch them file in and find seats.

But today I had to set up the conference room myself. The long rectangular table had to be cleared. There were ashtrays, pads and pencils, and Styrofoam coffee cups neatly arranged about a bowl of plastic flowers which sat directly below a large, circular light that fit flush into the ceiling. It was an amazing fixture. The light throughout the room was radiant. No corner escaped intense brightness. Yet you could stare directly into the circle without hurting your eyes. Also it was controlled by a dimmer, so I could regulate the brightness.

I removed the flowers, the pads, the pencils, the ashtrays, and the cups and stored them in a side table. Then I dimmed the light halfway and marveled at the absolutely even distribution of twilight that remained.

There was a Mr. Coffee machine on top of the side table. Mrs. P., if she remembered at all, would notice that that was the only change in the room since she had been there. The large silver-plated urn which dispensed percolated coffee into substantial earthenware mugs had given way last year to the more economical, more convenient, more efficient Mr. Coffee and the high-rise nest of unbreakable Styrofoam containers which freed my secretary from dishwashing duty. I filled the machine with a bag of coffee and a pot of water and turned it on.

At the front of the room stood my easel. The moderator's easel. I placed a fresh crayon on the ledge beneath the tear-away sheets of manilla paper that were fixed to the easel. I moved the easel a few inches just so that I felt I had positioned it.

Too many chairs. This was to be an in-depth focus interview of one. A universe of one. Only one chair was necessary. All the others I pulled away from the table and pushed back to the walls.

Next I had to remove the tape recorder and jerry-built boom device. We had simply strung the microphone cord to the ceiling with a screw hook. At first the members were conscious of the mike dangling overhead. But eventually they forgot about it in a way that passing a table mike around from speaker to speaker made impossible. Long ago we used to camouflage the microphone at the center of the table, but the clatter of cups and the drumming of fingers interfered. The boom was an inspiration; somehow the voice of the panelists floated upward while the rest of the noise kept mysteriously at tabletop level.

I put the recording equipment in the kitchenette, which stood between the conference room and the monitoring room. Then I went to see if the view through the one-way mirror matched the image I had in my mind of the conference room. I entered the darkness of the monitoring room.

As I flicked on the chandelier, I illuminated a full fifty percent of the company's capital investment: a long, plush sofa covered in velvet; small, Oriental end tables supporting Tiffany-style lamps; a glass-top coffee table; two enormous brass ashtrays; matching armchairs, three; a Persian area rug; and the console—the custom-built console that stretched the entire length of the mirrored wall. Four leather director's chairs fit the console as if it were their desk, two on each side, flanking the center bar which displayed every man's poison. The big drink for the last several years was vodka, because it left our clients breathless. (In a session to determine the advertising strategy for a Canadian whiskey, I learned that the copy line "It leaves you breathless" translated to vodka drinkers as "It doesn't leave any trace of liquor on your breath.") So among the aperitifs and liqueurs and fancy mixers and fancier decanters and brass ice bucket and crystal glassware were at least five quarts of the invisible elixir of the day. (What good would it have done to smell the sailor's or my wife-to-be's breath?)

On top of the desk areas of the console were scientifically shaded panel lights so clients could make notes, or see how much ice they had left in their glasses, or do crossword puzzles, or work on some other business project without the group members' being able to detect the life behind the one-way mirror.

The curtains were drawn over my side of the one-way mirror. They were thick curtains with Miro-like patterns in blues, yellows, reds, and blacks. Out of habit I turned off the chandelier and made sure no other light was on before pressing the console button that powered the curtain pulls. Slowly, silently, they parted and withdrew, unveiling the scene of the seduction. The light inside the conference room was soft and full. The woodgrain Formica tabletop gleamed below the glowing light. The one black vinyl chair looked ominously important where I had placed it, immediately to the right of the easel. Mr. Coffee was just beginning to produce a potful of black, steaming coffee.

The phone. I couldn't believe it. Two rings. Three. Could it possibly be Mrs. P. to say she wasn't coming? Or the police to say they were?

I hurried to the reception area, but I knew I was not going to answer the phone. Family. That's who it must be. Of course. They couldn't get me at home so they called the only other number they had. They want to visit. They want to announce another lost toe. They want to know where we all are and why we're not where we're supposed to be. They want to make sure we're okay.

I waited for the phone to stop ringing. It was an elaborate model with several buttons. The middle button flashed every time there was a ring. No. It flashed between rings, too. The quick, urgent flashing made the caller more real. I pictured my mother's finger tapping nervously on the countertop in her kitchen. She was never coy about it. It was always her middle finger, the biggest one, and she'd just keep pounding it against the countertop over and over and over again as if she were hammering a nail. She was never one to cover up her worry. Her nerves stuck out of every pore. Middle button. Middle finger. Tap tap. Flash flash. Tap tap.

I limped into the bathroom. During all my preparations in the conference room, before that, too, while I was going through the transcript, the pain in my toe had not bothered me. But now, as suddenly as the ringing and flashing and tapping, the pain was back. The toe throbbed. The pain was thin, as if it were bone rather than flesh that ached. Was bone a better conductor of pain? I didn't know. But the pain screamed through my body as I closed out the noise of the phone with the bathroom door. A new noise began, the fan. It automatically hummed when the bathroom door closed. The light went on automatically, too. But the ringing stopped. Or else I couldn't hear it.

I peed. It was a good long one, and it felt better and better the closer I got to the end. A wet little postscript stained my pants, but the spot would dry and disappear. Unlike the lollipop spot on my lapel. I rubbed it with cold water but I could still see the original stain in the center of the big new watermark.

I inched the door open, afraid the phone would still be ringing. Only twice before had I ever purposely let a phone ring. Today, when I was leaving the house. And once long ago, when we were on our honeymoon. We were making love for the second time that night, our dinners lying uneaten on the aluminum room-service tray beside the bed. It must have been toward the end of the week. I remembered how tan our arms and legs and her back were. When the phone rang, I groaned, and she put her finger to my lips and urged me to ignore the ringing. And I did. The next morning I asked at the desk if the caller had left a message, and when the clerk said "Sorry," I called everyone who knew where we were staying, until finally I had to admit to myself that it might have been a mistake, perhaps the clerk had put the call through to the wrong room, my room.

But in neither case had I fled from the phone. Both times I had better, more pressing alternatives.

I hobbled to my office to wait, thinking that if I sat fairly still in friendly surroundings I wouldn't disturb my physical appearance. Besides, I wanted to find out a little more about Mrs. P.

Every member of the group was required to fill out a biographical form. It occurred to me that I had never looked at Mrs. P.'s. If she had a daughter the age of Evelyn Pfeiffer, it would be on that form. Along with incidental information such as her husband's occupation, his salary level, her education, her work history. I found the form in the folder that was already spread open on my desk.

Mrs. P. had three children, two boys and a girl. The girl might be approximately the same age as Miss Subways, but it would take some stretching. Mrs. P. herself was forty-six now. Her husband worked for the Department of Welfare. His job was to locate missing husbands. She had actually written that down. He locates missing husbands, when Department of Welfare would have been sufficient. But she was proud. Or else she felt an explanation of his duties might compensate, in the eyes of the reader, for the meager salary her husband earned. She finished high school, took a correspondence course in shorthand, but had never worked a day in her life.

These new facts sneaked into my mind. I was not saying them over and over to myself, but I knew they were registering.

A few minutes to go. Mrs. P. should be in the vicinity of the building. And then I sat up straight in my chair. What about the building attendant? He might not let her up. What should I do?

I wanted to run, fly, downstairs and tell the attendant that I was expecting her. But what if I accidentally met her down there as she was coming in? I didn't know why, but it was important for her to come to my place, not meet me in a public lobby.

But my panic was all for nothing. The doorbell rang. She was here. My date, my angel, the belle of my prom was here.

•

I could not get up.

The bell rang again, and I was terrified she would leave. But I was frozen to my chair.

"Come in," I shouted, but I knew she couldn't hear me. In desperation, I pressed the paging button on my phone and heard a tinny voice explode throughout every office.

"OPEN THE DOOR, MRS. PALAEO. IT'S UNLOCKED. OPEN THE DOOR AND COME IN."

There was a moment or two of silence. I assumed she had heard me. But I had to know for sure.

"PICK UP THE PHONE AND PRESS ANY BUTTON, MRS. PALAEO," my voice clanged.

Another moment passed. And then a button lit up on my phone. It seemed to light up inside of me as well. I volunteered a dumbfounded little laugh. She was in the reception area. She was at the desk. More than that. She was so intimidated by the blackmail threat that she was listening to me without my even being there. Mrs. P. Mrs. Panic. She had actually pushed the panic button.

But what about me? Wasn't I panicking too? Why couldn't I move?

"JUST . . . IF . . . UH, Y—I'M GLAD YOU CAME, MRS. PALAEO."

I could move. I didn't want to. Desperation had turned to invention had turned to relief had turned to excitement. There was the beginning of a thrill in remaining out of sight. The thrill was in the delicate balance between risk and safety. At first it tipped toward the risk that Mrs. P. would leave, that my Wizard of Oz presence would scare her away. But the more I thought about it, and it was only a matter of seconds, the more I thought about what the two of us were doing there, the better I liked being safely incognito. Just how far could I get?

"ON YOUR RIGHT," I knew she was standing in front of the reception desk, "THERE IS A WHITE DOOR AND AN OAK DOOR, MRS. PALAEO. TAKE THE WHITE DOOR AND WALK HALFWAY DOWN THE CORRIDOR."

I was amazed at how well I knew every inch of the office. It would take about twenty Mrs. P.-sized steps to reach the halfway point of the corridor. I counted them off to myself. I allowed for the fact that she was probably as uncertain as if she were walking through pitch blackness. Then I told her to enter the room marked Conference.

"THERE'S A FRESH POT OF COFFEE, MRS. PALAEO. SEE IT? IT'S ON THE TABLE ALL THE WAY ACROSS THE ROOM. PICK UP THE PHONE IF YOU SEE THE COFFEE."

A horrible thought. Sometimes the paging network was turned off in the conference room so that routine office communication wouldn't interrupt an interview. If one of my buttons lit up, that meant Mrs. P. could still hear me.

I watched my phone.

Nothing.

Maybe she couldn't find the phone.

"THE PHONE IS RIGHT NEXT TO THE COFFEE."

Still nothing. And then a button lit up.

I heard myself sigh. And then the light disappeared.

"EVERYTHING YOU NEED IS UNDER THE TABLE, ON THE BOTTOM SHELF. THERE'S A STYROFOAM CUP, A PLASTIC STIRRER, TWO PACKETS OF SUGAR SUBSTITUTE—THAT SHOULD BE PLENTY, IT'S SWEETER THAN THE REAL STUFF—AND SOME CREAM. IT'S POWDERED CREAM, MRS. PALAEO. BUT IT'S NOT BAD."

I wondered if I had planned it this way, and, if not, why I hadn't foreseen the magic of it. Here I was, sitting at my desk, leafing through papers, doodling on my from-the-office-of pad, cradling the receiver with my left shoulder, my right, back again, a routine business call, not really listening, not really caring, yet caring more than I ever had, actually becoming sexually aroused. I could feel the little downbeat in my pants.

"I KNOW YOU MUST BE A BIT CONFUSED, MRS. PALAEO. LET ME TRY TO ANSWER SOME OF THE QUESTIONS THAT MUST BE RUNNING THROUGH YOUR MIND."

Suddenly there *was* a plan. First I would make her trust me, reassure her that her extorted visit was on the up-and-up. Then I would make her understand that she was trapped. Then I would make my play for her, dazzle her with how much I knew about her, how meant for each other we were, get her in the mood, waltz her around like Fred Astaire. And then—then—my grand entrance. At that point she would be crazy with desire.

"FIRST OF ALL, WHO AM I? I'M THE MAN WHO PICKED YOU OUT OF TWELVE WOMEN, MRS. PALAEO, BECAUSE YOU WERE THE MOST GENUINE, THE PRETTIEST IN YOUR OWN WAY, THE MOST DEVOTED."

I imagined how my compliment must have terrified her. Compliments always do.

"DID I SAY TWELVE? EVERY WOMAN, MRS. PALAEO, I PICKED YOU OUT OF EVERY WOMAN I KNOW."

That was a lie. I hadn't really considered anyone else. But I might have. Deborah, for example. She'd spend the night with me again in a second. Except Deborah lives in Cleveland. (I'm even wearing the shirt we picked out at that thrift shop). And Kathy lives in Buffalo. And Rosemary's too much in love with that architect of hers. And Marilyn Monroe, even if she were alive—. And I haven't seen Dolores since the third grade. And the one or two whores I've known are probably in jail. Or dead. Or married.

"I'M NOT THE MAN WHO ASKED YOU QUESTIONS THREE YEARS AGO, MRS. PALAEO. HE'S NO LONGER WITH THE COMPANY. HE WAS GAY AS A GOAT, AND SOMETIMES HIS BITCHINESS BIASED THE INTERVIEWS."

That was the truth. If properly controlled, his gay charm put women at ease, especially women who had to talk about feminine products and behaviors. But when that moderator lost control, which he did more and more frequently during the last year, those same women found themselves trapped in a room with someone who lorded his cock over them. It was the strangest thing. He longed to be one of them, but only up to a point. And then he'd snicker with gratitude because he didn't have to put up with disposable douches, or bra cups that promised to wear like air and work like plaster, or, worst of all, the degrading choice of having to label a flow junior, regular, or super.

"THOSE OTHER ELEVEN WOMEN IN YOUR GROUP, YOU'RE WONDERING WHERE THEY ARE. BACK HOME, I GUESS, MRS. PALAEO. SAFE AND SOUND. STILL HOPING, PRAYING, SAYING THAT A LITTLE PEE SHIVER IN THE DEAD OF NIGHT IS AN AUTHENTIC RIPPLE OF ORGASM."

Not Mrs. P. The P does not stand for pretend.

"WHY YOU, MRS. PALAEO? WHY DID I SAY SUCH TERRIBLE THINGS TO YOU ON THE PHONE? BELIEVE ME, I ONLY SAID WHAT I HAD TO IN ORDER TO GET YOU HERE. I WAS AFRAID YOU WOULDN'T COME."

I was afraid she'd leave if I didn't get on with it.

"YOU SEE, MRS. PALAEO, MY WIFE LEFT ME LAST NIGHT. SHE TOOK THE KIDS WITH HER. AND NOW HERE IT IS, ALMOST SATURDAY NIGHT," I had no idea what I was going to say, but there were a million dissassociated phrases, thoughts, ideas, feelings, too, all circuiting and cross-circuiting in my brain, "AND I DON'T HAVE A DATE."

My button lit up.

"MRS. PALAEO, DON'T BE AFRAID. YOU'RE NOT IN ANY DANGER. PUT DOWN THE PHONE, IT WON'T HELP. AND DON'T TRY TO RUN AWAY, THAT WON'T HELP EITHER. I JUST WANT TO BE WITH YOU, DON'T YOU SEE? I NEED TO BE CLOSE TO SOMEONE WHO UNDERSTANDS. SOMEONE WHO WON'T FIGHT IT. AS LONG AS YOU STAY IN THE CONFERENCE ROOM AND DO AS I SAY EVERYTHING WILL BE FINE. I CAN'T EVEN SEE YOU, MRS. PALAEO. THAT'S HOW MUCH I TRUST YOU. IF YOU WERE TO TAKE OFF ALL YOUR CLOTHES AND STRETCH OUT ON THE CONFERENCE ROOM TABLE, ONLY YOU AND THE WALLS WOULD KNOW, MRS. PALAEO. BUT IF YOU TRY TO ESCAPE, ANYTHING CAN HAPPEN. YOU MIGHT EVEN MAKE IT. BUT THEN, WHAT ABOUT THE SECRET ABORTION YOU CONFESSED TO IN THE FOCUS GROUP INTERVIEW? YOU KNOW WHAT THAT WOULD DO TO YOUR HUSBAND."

The lit button died.

"THE FUNNY THING IS, MRS. PALAEO, I'M WILLING TO BET THAT YOU HAD THAT ABORTION FOR YOUR HUSBAND'S SAKE. IT MUST BE PRETTY TOUGH 'TO RAISE THREE KIDS ON THE MONEY HE MAKES. FOUR WOULD HAVE BROKEN THE CAMEL'S BACK. INSTEAD OF LOOKING FOR MISSING HUSBANDS, HE'D BE ONE, WOULDN'T HE?"

What was she doing? Could I count on her to behave the way she was supposed to? Was she going to laugh and cry and love me in all the right places? Could I hold out a little longer before I had to rush into the conference room to see with my own eyes? And would I smack into the wall like Mr. Magoo?

"SHE LEFT ME BECAUSE OF YOU, MRS. PALAEO," I said matter-of-factly, letting the content of my casual remark provide the entire drama. "I COULDN'T BEAR ANOTHER TICK OF THE CLOCK ALONE. I NEEDED TO BE WITH YOU."

These words did not nearly measure up to the words I felt, and I was disappointed in myself. I wanted Mrs. P. to like me, feel a bit sorry for me, but I was too smooth. I should have told her that I worshipped her, women like that. I should have explained that although my wife had never known a thing about my other women, she suffered the silent comparisons I'd made: wife anguished, Mrs. P.

at peace; wife filled with self-hate, Mrs. P. full of selfless love; wife trapped by her wisdom, Mrs. P. ignorantly thus blissfully free; wife dead, Mrs. P. alive.

"ARE YOU STILL THERE, MRS. PALAEO?"

I forgot that I wasn't actually talking to her on the phone.

"OF COURSE YOU'RE THERE. YOU'RE ALWAYS THERE. IN THE MORNING. AT DINNER. AT BEDTIME, TOO. YOUR JOB IS TO BE THERE. YOUR MISSION IS TO BE THERE. YOUR LIFE IS TO BE THERE. THE HUNGRIER YOUR HUSBAND GETS, THE HIGHER THE BILLS PILE UP, THE MORE DISRESPECTFUL AND STUBBORN THE CHILDREN GROW, THE BETTER YOU LIKE IT."

Does she understand? Make her understand.

"MY WIFE IS IN THAT EXACT SAME SITUATION, BUT SHE FIGHTS IT, AND THAT MAKES HER LIFE TRAGIC. YOU ACCEPT IT, AND THAT MAKES YOU A SAINT, MRS PALAEO. IT MAKES THE MAN YOU'RE WITH A GOD."

The P stands for purity. Patience. Protection.

"WHY DO YOU THINK I RAN TO YOU LIKE A LITTLE BOY WHO HURTS HIMSELF RUNS TO HIS MOTHER? BECAUSE YOU ARE THE VERY MEANING OF THE WORD."

The word inside the sexless moan. Love without orgasm. She had said it herself: mothers don't have orgasms, they just satisfy their . . .

"I BET," I fixed the crotch of my pants so my penis was freer to erect, "I BET MEN HAVE ALWAYS BEEN ATTRACTED TO YOU, MRS. PALAEO."

God, I was. I swear I could feel the semen rising like mercury in a thermometer.

"I BET THEY ALL WANT TO SAY FUCK YOU TO THEIR WIVES WHEN THEIR WIVES COMPLAIN ABOUT A HEADACHE OR HOW TIRED THEY ARE OR HOW THE KIDS REALLY RAN ME RAGGED TODAY—FUCK YOU, I'M GETTING OUT OF HERE. I'M GOING TO LOOK UP THIS FANTASTIC LITTLE NUMBER BY THE NAME OF PALAEO, SHE DOESN'T HAVE A HEADACHE, SHE NEVER GETS TIRED, SHE AIMS TO PLEASE. THAT'S BECAUSE SHE DOESN'T EVER WEAR HERSELF OUT TRYING TO HAVE AN ORGASM. SHE'LL TAKE ME IN. SHE'LL MAKE IT ALL BETTER."

My button lit up. Out again. On again.

I pictured her naked, swimming underwater. Her arms (was it possible?) were not visible to me. Perhaps she held them behind her back as a sign of how unashamed she was. But arms more than anything signified sexuality to me. They might caress one's own body, or beckon for love, or deliver love one finger at a time—oh, at that mere thought my penis stretched itself like my cat. A thousand emotions shot through me as I watched the button blink frantically on and off. I was confused. I was out of control. I was weak. I was on the brink of crying, laughing, ejaculating, screaming, throwing up. The room started to spin. I felt my chair shake. I closed my eyes and looked into the mirrored captain's wheel; I threw off my purple coverlet; I stared deep within the concentric rings of brown and pink in the oval rug; I peeked between the shutters to see if Ray's car had pulled in behind my mother's; the rose walls seemed to be tipping backwards ever so slightly, threatening to crash to the ground like a Hollywood set. I saw myself clutch my living dagger and brandish it menacingly at a cowering female figure, bring it down into the flesh of my pillow again and again and again like boy/mother Bates in *Psycho;* I timed the stabs with the shuddering beats of love's mad song, with the frantic flashing of the button.

"MAKE IT BETTER, MRS. PALAEO. MAKE IT ALL BETTER. PLEASE. TAKE OFF YOUR CLOTHES. LET ME SEE YOU. LET ME SMELL YOU. LET ME GET INSIDE YOU. PLEASE."

And then suddenly I understood the real reason why I hadn't been able to move: I was scared to death. I was terrified that she wouldn't make it all better. That she wouldn't get undressed. That she wouldn't love me, no matter what. So I hid. I hid behind work. I hid behind my one-way mirror. I hid behind a louder voice and stronger muscles and a bigger appetite for life. My entire presence was a hidden threat. Day by day, hour by hour, minute by minute, I killed her. I made her believe that there was no hope. That the only escape was the dumb luck to be born ignorant, to inherit a natural blind acceptance, a genetic slaphappiness like Mrs. P.'s.

"DON'T."

I popped to my feet like a body pops to the surface of water. On my aching toe I ran out of the office down the corridor to the conference room and flung open the door. The first thing I saw was myself in the wall-length mirror opposite the door. My face was red and blurry, my clothes looked too big and sopping wet. And then my eyes bulged into focus as I saw my reflection turn to Mrs. P. I was sure I was standing still, startled by the wild sight of myself, and yet my reflection ran to Mrs. P.'s slumped, sobbing body. One of her hands was in the middle of unbuttoning her blouse. The other was depressing and releasing and depressing and releasing both disconnect buttons on top of the phone in a desperate reflex action that made me think of rigor mortis. When she saw my reflection approaching, she screamed and clutched the collars of her blouse to her neck with clenched fists, as though sealing off the entrance to her secret, sacred self. Then she stopped in the middle of the scream, her eyes frozen on me, her entire body locked in dread.

Only my eyes moved as I looked us up and down in the mirror. It might have been the end of a dance, the two of us waiting patiently, breathlessly for darkness to flood the stage so we could slip unnoticed into the wings. Until then we were trained not to move a muscle.

But instead of darkness, I saw something that drove every bit of breath and blood out of my body.

"Hnahh," I cried out involuntarily.

All I could do was point. I pointed at the spot in the mirror. I fell back against the wall, still pointing, still gaping at the spot where I had seen it. I was paralyzed. I was catatonic. I thought I'd never blink again. I thought my heart would pound itself out of my chest as it pumped fear through every artery. Panic hit like a sudden drop in temperature. A tiny light burned a hole behind my eyes through the center of my brain. It was still alive. It burned like a cigarette hole in a piece of cellophane, a raggedy red circle relentlessly expanding into whiter and whiter nothingness. More light, dazzling, blinding, poured through the opening. The light illuminated the face of my wife, the faces of our children; they were crying out to me, but I was in shadows beyond the red glow.

"The click," I tried to say out loud, but couldn't. "Remember I heard a click, Mrs. Palaeo? Who was listening in on the telephone? Who was it, Mrs. Palaeo?"

But, of course, she couldn't hear me.

"Someone's in that room," I said silently. "Someone's watching us, Mrs. Palaeo. I saw a light. A tiny light, Mrs. Palaeo, it flared into a flame for just an instant and disappeared. Someone is back there. Someone is sitting in the monitoring room watching everything we do. Everything we've done. Who, Mrs. Palaeo? Who heard us on the phone? Who knew we were here? Who followed you?"

"WHO?" I shouted, and the word roared out of my mouth like a rumble of thunder.

I picked up the easel and swung it into the mirror. The glass cracked but did not shatter. Again I hit it with the easel. Another crack. And again. And another crack. Finally I threw the useless easel across the room and goose-ran to the door of the kitchenette. I flung it open and made for a second door, the one that led into the monitoring room. When I got inside I searched the darkness for a mysterious shadow. Nothing moved. No one breathed. The perfect order of the darkened room mocked me.

I flicked on the light switch and the chandelier burst into brightness. On the glass-top table, in the huge brass ashtray, a cigarette anchored a silvery trail of smoke that tried to escape into the chandelier's blinding aura.

"Look at this," I said, picking up the cigarette and showing it to Mrs. P. We stared at each other for a long time through the cracked glass. "Look," I said, pointing its red glow at her.

It was all over; the panic, the outrage, the fury, all of it disappeared. I limped back into the conference room. The blood returned. Breath returned. A sadness stooped my shoulders, bowed my head, worked its way out through my eyes. I kept picturing my older boy trying in vain to whistle.

When I stood before Mrs. P., I saw that she too was crying, had been for a number of years.

I examined the cigarette, took a long, deep drag, dropped it to the floor, and crushed it out with the heel of my bad foot.

I knelt down beside Mrs P. and began buttoning her blouse.

"Who do you know that smokes Virginia Slims?" I asked quietly, almost tenderly.

Mrs. P. looked up at me. Her eyes were the saddest I had ever seen.

"Don't hurt me," she whimpered. "Please, don't hurt me."

"No, Sweet Pea, no," I whispered. "It's all right, Sweet Pea, all right, Sweet Pea, all right, Sweet Pea . . ." Then I held her, and we rocked to the rhythm of her sobs until they were gone.

Sunday

t was dark, but I had no trouble seeing.

The ground was a tangle of splintered gray slats and broken vines. The holes were still open, or shark-toothed tips of violently snapped stakes stuck up a few inches to mark the unrobbed graves of dying tomatoes; their vines were severed like the veins in my wife's wrists. In the graveyard moonlight, the insides of the shattered gray slats showed an unweathered white, almost the same color as the moon. Almost the same unweathered color of a newborn infant, before life adds gray.

One by one, in order of length and loft, I planted the three-quarter-sized golf clubs where Otto's stakes had stood a day ago. First the driver, then the three wood, the four wood, the two iron, the three, four, five, six, seven, eight, and nine irons, the pitching wedge, the sand wedge, the putter. Occasionally I dug out a menacing, barely buried shark tooth and replaced it with a club.

It was the middle of the human night, early Sunday morning by the clock, and I had been traveling for many hours.

Mrs. P. had taken a while to quiet down sufficiently to talk and listen for a while. I had told her how sorry I was, that I must have gone into a mad shock when I found my wife and kids were gone. She had said she could understand and that actually, apart from her nerves and the lying note on the kitchen table and the remote possibility that her daughter had overheard our telephone conversation and followed Mrs. P. to my office—her daughter smoked Virginia Slims, but so did a lot of other people—no real harm had been done.

"Harm," I had said solemnly, handing her twelve dollars to cover her carfare, "is done long before we realize it," and then I walked her to the door.

139

We rode down the elevator together, the bag of golf clubs I had bought for my youngest son rattling on my shoulder as I kept shifting weight off my painful foot. When we reached the street, I flagged a taxi for her. She even shook my hand through the half-opened window before the taxi lurched into the dinner hour traffic jam.

"Good-bye, Sweet Pea," I whispered after she could not hear; my hand remained poised in the handshake, her forgiving touch still upon it like the chill of a great truth.

When at last I turned away, heart hoping against head that Mrs. P. could start her life again, I began walking. I seemed to be the only single person on the street; everyone else walked in twos or threes or foursomes, laughing, hugging, hailing cabs, window-shopping, sharing the sweet, warm, twinkling twilight of the city. Straight down the center of the sidewalk I limped, unintentionally crashing the oncoming parties, silently wishing them well as grudgingly they separated to let me pass or quickly bunny-hopped around me.

At the first bar, I made my first stop. The hatcheck girl made me check my golf bag; after my bourbon she caught me halfway out the door and made me redeem the bag. I was tempted to wave her back and say forget it. Without having been able to explain why, I sensed that the clubs had been a mistake. But I paid for them with a half dollar and put them next on the empty barstool beside mine in the second bar I came to.

In all, I played through nine watering holes on my way to the train station. After four, I switched from bourbon to beer, though nothing I drank seemed to affect me. No one talked to me either. Except for perfunctory what'll-it-be's from the bartenders, I might have been invisible. When finally, in a sour-smelling, too dark bar somewhere on Thirty-fourth Street, an unpretty girl did try to strike up a conversation, I hardly noticed her. After her three weak jokes about my golf bag drew neither laughter nor an offer to buy her a drink, she flitted to the arm of a conventioneer from St. Louis. (In the early years of our marriage, when my wife and I spent many nights out on the town, we always identified anyone who didn't look like he belonged as a conventioneer from St. Louis.)

By the time I reached the train station I had downed progres-

sively rougher bourbon and warmer beer through the end of Saturday; my last train, the 12:10, was receiving passengers on track
number seven. As I limped and rattled toward the red-lit seven at
the top of the stairway leading down to the track, I felt as though
I were wading through a huge aquarium. The inhabitants of the
station were absolutely silent as they darted and glided beneath
glaring incandescence or sat suspended on one-legged chairs or
floated about the big schedule board, the newsboy, the all-night
pizza stand, the bathrooms, the information booth. Unlike the mad
jam of nearly entangled commuters I was used to threading in order
to catch my usual 5:37 or 6:15, or even 7:05, they avoided touching
one another, like different species.

The train was new and sleek and looked like a jet inside with its
carpeted floor, reclining armchairs, fold-down trays, inlaid reading
lights, hidden ashtrays, and air conditioning that sounded like de-
pressurization.

The car I had picked was empty except for a sailor. I sat down
next to him. I wondered if he minded. I wondered if, in the past,
the strangers who had picked me to sit next to in otherwise empty
trains had also just found their families murdered the night before,
and had also just come from blackmail, near rape, a drinking binge.

But the sailor had been genuinely happy to have company. He
was just a kid. He was on his way to Philadelphia to see his girl before a six-month tour on a nuclear submarine, of all things.

"Nuclear, huh?"

"Yes, sir."

"What does that mean exactly. What's the name of the submarine?"

"I really can't talk about it, sir."

No one but waitresses and shoe clerks ever called me sir. I liked
the sailor.

"Got a girl in every port, I suppose?"

"Oh no, sir. Just Evelyn."

I hadn't been surprised by the coincidence of names, his Evelyn
in Philly and my Evelyn Pfeiffer; by then I had come to believe that
coincidences were actually the coming together of all the pieces.
I was experiencing the "other side" of my trip into the city as
though this trip were the other side of the moon, the light side.

Evelyn had turned from a flapping, pterodactylic figment to a real-life Penelope. The sailor had turned from a boastful, brutal woman-izer into a gentle and loyal young man from some nuclear tomor-rowland. Even the sights I glimpsed out of the freezing, fogging, convex windows seemed to include everything I had ordinarily missed on countless train rides home. More than once I panicked that I'd gotten onto the wrong train.

"I missed the service both times. Too young for Korea, two bum legs for Vietnam."

The sailor used my remark to ask about my foot.

"No, that's something else. You might even say that this one's a war wound," I mused aloud, stretching my poor leg out into the aisle.

He had too much respect to question me further about my strange reference to my even stranger half shoe and filthy toes.

"My little boy—I have two, seven and four—my little one's crazy about boats. You should have seen him when all those boats came down the river to celebrate the Bicentennial."

At that moment, recalling how the sight of those majestic ships had thrilled my little boy so that he could only laugh to express his incredible good fortune, I became sick. I had to run from my seat next to the sailor as fast as possible to keep from throwing up all over him and the silver and maroon chairs and the matching car-peting.

I locked myself in the lavatory and doubled over and held on and heaved up my drinks and the bit of food I'd eaten. And then I threw up nothing. Air. Poison. History. Again and again, as the train rolled through darkness, my body convulsed.

After a while there was a knock on the door, and, when I opened it, the sailor was standing at attention, my golf bag at his side like a rifle at parade rest, a soldierly look of brave concern on his blond face. It had been like looking at the precise moment in time when a face changes from a boy's to a man's. The two images had seemed slightly superimposed so that one second the sailor was seven or eight years old and the next second he was eighteen.

"Are you all right, sir? You said this was your station."

"Thank you," I said hoarsely, with the unabashed self-pity of someone whose body is not functioning properly. "Thank you, you're a good boy," I said, taking the bag, avoiding his eyes.

I took the stairs slowly, the bag bouncing behind me from step to step, producing an absurd sound effect for my painful descent. I sounded like a robot whose broken insides clanged and rattled with every movement.

That had been barely an hour ago. The streets had been deserted except for taxis and a college girl who had gotten off at my stop, caught up to me, and walked along as though she, too, were heading for the parking lot. She wore a clinging T-shirt that showed her nipples. She had no purse, no bag, nothing at all save whatever money or identification she might have had stuffed into the pockets of her skintight jeans.

She stopped, making me stop.

"Listen," she said, "we'll probably never see each other again for the rest of our lives, and I just want to tell you that you really have very beautiful, very kind eyes."

I blinked them.

"Do you have your car here?"

"Yes," I said, pointing to the not yet visible lot just around the corner of the block we'd been walking.

We were standing beneath the trestle. The train pulled out above us with booming chords of the new music. I had to strain to hear her soft request.

"Could I have a lift?" she said.

Everything I then said had had a hidden meaning, a less sinister meaning so much more difficult to voice.

I said: "Where to?"

I meant: "I hope you don't live far, what if I hadn't happened along? If I were your father I'd be worried sick to think of you wandering these streets at this hour."

I said: "Do you live in one of the dorms or in your own apartment?"

I meant: "Will there be someone waiting for you? Making sure you're okay? Welcoming you home? Putting an arm around you?"

The effect of my half of the conversation had been evil sounding to me. I sounded like a lecher. I kept looking at her nipples. Yet she was not afraid.

I said: "Do you always ask strangers for a lift?"

I meant: "Aren't you afraid of me? I am. Afraid of me. Of what I might do."

She never said a word about the bag of rattling clubs between us as we started walking again. I led her slightly, but tried to keep my eyes on her jiggling breasts and pointy nipples. Sometime deep in my past I had taken a tight nipple between my teeth and bitten down as hard as possible without actually biting into the nipple. That's how it felt. Like wanting to eat up a baby. Couldn't you just bite it and squeeze it and hug it to death? But at the last moment you locked your aggressive adoration just short of actually hurting the object of your desire.

In the space of a few steps, I had come to regard my deliciously built and trusting coed as a test. Passing would have meant driving her home and making sure she was through her front door before I pulled away. But if I offered her a two o'clock snack (feeding), or a drink, or even a spin instead of a direct ride home, surely I would have been flirting with failure on a much grander scale than merely whether or not she might have accepted. But I never had the choice.

At the corner I automatically glanced at the parking lot to check my car. It wasn't in its usual space. Panic. I remembered that I had parked in another spot. Nowhere. Real panic. I ran ahead, but I knew that my car was gone. That sonofabitching old stumblebum had stuck to his guns and called his nephew. I looked all around the streets, thinking maybe my car had only been towed out into a public parking spot. Funny how attached you could become to a machine. It actually hurt me, made my stomach sink, to think of strangers recklessly cranking my personal property up off the ground and yanking it on skidding hind wheels to some junkyard prison. A few hours ago, as the train flew out of the interstate tunnel, one of the first sights I remembered not seeing before had been a mountainous graveyard of twisted, mashed, compacted, skeletal automobiles. If I neglected to find the whereabouts of my car, rescue the nervous beast, then one day soon its shiny white chassis and jet plane dash would sigh their last high atop the gull-guarded compost of cars that welcomed the world to New Jersey.

Papa Car was nowhere in sight. I turned back to the young girl who had remained across the street, her eyes searching first one and then the opposite direction of the main avenue.

"My car's been towed away," I said when I rejoined her. "What should we do?"

"It's all right," she said. "I'll get home."

And she stepped out into the avenue.

"What are you going to do?" I asked her.

The first car that came along stopped right in front of her. I couldn't hear what she said to the three men crowded into the front seat. One of them got out, closing the passenger side door behind him, and opened the rear door for himself and the girl. In the lamplight I saw that he was young, as young as she, probably no more than a sophomore at the same university.

All I had been able to think of were Red and Chicorski and Stu and how the first two were going to get their friend initiated.

"Thanks, anyway," I heard her call amidst the screech and fumes of burning rubber.

Based on the incongruity of the one boy's sloppy dress yet finely tailored politeness in opening the door and escorting the breasty coed inside, I was sure she had never laid eyes on any of them before that very moment. But she had been as unafraid of them as she had been of me.

Was this, I wondered, twisting a six iron into the ground, the new breed of woman? If asked, I had to say that there was no way the naively brave young girl could escape a gang bang. But was it true? What would I have said about any sailor before meeting Evelyn's nuclear-powered boyfriend?

I had stood there out of the light, halfway between the train station and the parking lot, an enormous puddle suddenly gurgling out of a backed-up sewer in front of me. A cab pulled up, splashing some of the filthy puddle onto my feet, and the driver said, "Get in." Perhaps someone had sent him to look after me, to make sure I got home. "My husband," I heard in my head, "is standing on the sidewalk near the train station, just past the trestle, and his car has been towed away," the staticky radio voice continued. "You'll know him by the bag of golf clubs and the green lollipop in his lapel. He's tired and confused and upset with himself. Pick him up, take him home."

"Where to?" the cabby asked, shifting into gear.

I gave him my address, but ordered him to take a specific route. I'd tell him when and where to turn.

Unlike the New York cabs I was used to, this one had no meter, just a flat rate per destination. But no rates were posted inside the car. That was left to the discretion and honesty of the driver, and, I had assumed, haggling was okay.

But, of course, I would not haggle. I would pay him whatever he asked.

He was an old man, the driver, and, as far as I could tell from his incomplete reflection in the rearview mirror, he was not very clean. His face was gray, as though he hadn't washed for a very long time, with a darker gray caught in the crisscrossing creases of his cracked paint skin. His hair was stringy and uncombed and matted to his forehead above cavernous sockets. But his eyes belonged to a much younger man. They were intense and set to see a great distance in the dark. The combination of his powerful eyes and hard, sure fingers on the wheel convinced me that the cabby was stronger and more vigorous than he looked.

"Here. Pull over," I directed him when the taxi approached the Heaven on Earth Church of the Pentateuch.

I had asked the dutiful driver to wait for me, and wondered how this interruption would affect the fare without a meter to register the gas and time it might take for me to visit the church. But I didn't care if he charged me all my money.

The front door of Heaven on Earth was unlocked. I entered and made my way forward, more with caution than surprise, because of the darkness inside. A hairline crack of light wavered vertically in a far corner, otherwise the converted storefront was unrelentingly black.

After stumbling into a bridge chair, I realized that there were no pews, and, after groping down an aisle which took me closer and closer to the crack of light and the indistinct sounds and sight which tried to trickle through, I realized that there was not a raised altar either.

I had gone there to make a last confession, but found no confessional, no priest. I knelt at the first row of chairs, not far from the door that was open just a crack, not far from the mumblings behind the door. When I began my confession, outwardly silent, but loud and clear in my mind's ear, the other voices reminded me of a drifting channel. I was tuned in to my symbolic unburdening (no priest could have understood what I confessed without an elaborate explanation), but my attention was regularly distracted by the ghostly hum of unintelligible voices that kept drifting into my frequency. What had they been saying?

When the disturbance finally made me look in the direction of the voices, I saw thin cigarette smoke float through the crack of light. Occasionally someone shouted and banged on a table.

"I smoke Virginia Slims," I confessed. "The whole thing was a setup. There wasn't anyone behind the mirror. I lit that cigarette in the kitchenette, before I ever got to the monitoring room. But I did see a light. I just wanted to make sure that Mrs. P. saw it too."

Something "beat ladies," I thought I heard through the crack of light.

"My wife," I confessed, "smoked Virginia Slims. Every time I strayed I always had the feeling that my wife knew, even though I knew she'd never say anything. There was a crystal bowl filled with candy on Deborah's coffee table. My hand accidentally knocked it over while we were making love on the sofa. The bowl landed upside down on the floor, two cellophane-wrapped brown sucking candies caught underneath the cut crystal. Whenever I looked at it, I saw my wife's eyes watching us. Is it so impossible that it was my wife's spirit smoking behind the one-way mirror? Watching my dis-embodied voice undress Mrs. P.?"

"Jacks or better, suckers," drifted in.

"The gay moderator smoked Virginia Slims, too. Maybe he still hangs around the office on weekends. When I fired him, we had an awful fight."

"Nevuh sind a boy, muh mayan," a voice interfered. The voice was so deep and so loud it seemed to force the crack in the door wider, letting other voices stream out behind it through the greater light.

"Who you callin' boy?"

"Who you callin'? And wid dem cards, too! Hah!"

"Take a peek, baby. I thought I heard somethin' out there."

The door opened and the shadow of a woman entered Heaven on Earth. The light bent across the chairs and caught my kneeling body. As she came toward me, I recognized the purple, swollen face and scarlet dress of the poor woman who had been on the bad end of the beating.

"Church is closed," she said contemptuously, hands on hips.

"I'm the sailor, I'm the sophomore, I'm the pimp who beat you," I heard myself say out loud.

"He's prayin' or drunk or somethin'," she explained to four T-shirted black men when the sound of my voice summoned them from their private chapel to the tip of the nave where I remained kneeling. One of the men took charge, assuring the others with a gesture that he'd straighten everything out. The woman backed out of his way as he hitched his pants and strode confidently to my bended body.

"You know what time it is?" he asked me in the deep voice that had led the other voices moments earlier. But he didn't want an answer. "The church is closed. You got to go, friend."

"Let her come with me," I asked somewhat defiantly, without looking at the lady of the night—but we all knew who I meant. "Let me take her to a hospital. She needs treatment."

"Anything botherin' you, Flossie?" he asked her, his eyes still focused on mine.

"Uh-uh," she said. "No, sir!" she said enthusiastically.

"You havin' a bad dream, mistah. You best take yourself home and sleep this one off," he boomed, his mouth working like those animals who want a Clark Bar, lips drawing back to reveal unreal flashes of smiling, gritting teeth within a barely moving jaw.

"They beat you," I said to her, trying to make her understand that she had been humiliated in front of the church, in front of all those people, in front of me.

The leader put his hands on my shoulders and raised me up. I offered no resistance. Then he led me back up the aisle that split the congregation into two equal sections.

"There's a lot you don't know 'bout that girl," he said, using his misleadingly friendly arm around my shoulders to make sure I left the church without turning back for any last appeal to the others. "See, what you don't know is that Flossie got her own car, uh huh. And a whole mess a pretty dresses. And all the pocket money she need." He cocked his head and grinned at me; he defied me not to understand what he was saying.

The instant I closed the car door behind me, the cab driver took off. He sped along streets I had never seen before. As often as I'd driven home from the station—two hundred and fifty times a year times how many years—as often as I'd experimented with different routes, the route the driver took was one that I had never tried. I had always thought that the streets he tore through were dead ends, or that they led to the river, or to wrongbound highways that would force me miles out of my way before I could get off and back on the right track. But the old man drove with the speedy confidence of someone who had been doing it all his life.

Every time he skidded around a corner, the clubs made a racket. On one turn the clubheads banged down onto my foot, and my head hit the window at the same time. But I had no complaints. In fact, I enjoyed the speed. There was something speeding inside of me that grew less panicky the more the physical world approximated the speed of my desire. Streets, cars, shops, houses, buildings hurried by at nearly the same rate as my desire to hurry home and be with my family.

One of my persistent daydreams always involved racing home to an emergency. I'd be working. The phone would ring. It would be horribly bad news, such as an automobile accident, a kidnapping, a fire—something brutal and potentially fatal—and I'd have to drop whatever I was doing and get back as fast as humanly possible. I would become a madman, knocking desks, telephones, easels, people out of my reckless path to the elevators. I'd keep pushing the damned DOWN button until the doors parted, and then I'd keep pushing the CLOSE button until the doors obeyed again. On the street I'd be an absolute wild man. Sometimes I'd take a subway, thinking it was faster than a taxi, but I'd commandeer a taxi anyway to get to the nearest subway entrance. Usually I grabbed an important-looking businessman by his coattails as he was entering the taxi and threw him down into the street, ordering the blasé cabby to step on it or else even before I was safely inside behind the slammed door. Of course, I'd run the bill. I'd run into the subway and jump the turnstile and bump people out of my way as I leaped down endless stairs to a train that always seemed to be just closing its doors. Like the last defender on a breakaway run from scrimmage, I'd hurl myself at the narrowing space between the doors. Forty-two minutes later I'd leap from the stopped train to my parked car in two or three superhuman bounds. I would create a physical correlative to the twisting, turning, weaving speed that churned my desperation, just as the cabdriver had done a half hour ago when he had tried to break the night barrier. It was startling how much my ride home from the church had felt like my daydream. The only difference was that in my daydream there was the giddy satisfaction of being able to break the law and then deal with it later. I had a real answer to "Where's the fire, Mac?" It really was a matter of life and death. No court in the land would dare convict a man on traffic violations if his wife lay dying, if his kids were choking on their gags, if his family was trapped by six-foot flames and collapsing walls.

But this time, this real time, I had no feeling of immunity. This time I had no excuse. I had the same blind sense of motion and mission, but no net below. If I fell, if I got caught, if any laws got broken, I could not say "They need me, my family needs me." Somewhere along the line I had missed my chance to say that.

•

I was jealous of Ray. By marrying him my mother had insinuated that I could not completely satisfy her. She needed more than I could offer. She did not love me *no matter what*.

It wasn't a jealous rage. In fact, I had never even realized what I felt until I began planting the sawed-off golf clubs in Otto's backyard; they reminded me of Ray and his sawed-off foot. I remembered the Sundays on the course, the days of theoretic chumminess during which we hardly saw or spoke to one another. I thought it might have been his natural hook and my natural slice that kept us on opposite sides of every fairway. But even on the greens, our true partners were our putters, our true audiences were our past selves who had, once upon a time, on days that will live as long as we do, broken ninety. Yet here I was bringing home the same instruments of solitude: little golf clubs for my little boy. Here I was providing him with what he needed in order not to need anyone else, and thinking that will make a man of him.

I tried to imagine another sport, another experience of any kind, in which total strangers spent hours together believing they were a twosome or threesome or foursome, when in fact the faces and names of the others are a blur right from the start and permanently erased by the final stroke. "Nice playin' with you." "Nice talkin' to you." "Nice seein' you." "Nice bein' with you." "Nice lovin' you." "Nice marryin' you." "Nice havin' children with you." "Nice bein' your daddy, boys."

After twisting and driving the last club into Otto's ravaged patch, I sat back, cross-legged, leaning on my hands. In contrast to Otto's explosive reaction to his dog's death, my reaction to the deaths of my wife and my sons had been mild—and unreal. I had devised a fantastic murder plot which involved exotic characters on both sides of the law—all this to glamorize, to conceal the pointlessness of my wife's act. Otto, on the other hand, had destroyed a plot with his bare hands. But some of my mad plotting had been intriguing. In particular, I remembered the knowing expression on Ray's face just before I imagined that he had been shot. What was he going to say before the sniper got him? Would I ever know? Had the very inconclusiveness of the scene been the point? And what about the guilt also on Ray's face at that moment, as if he were about to accuse himself as well as me?

In the darkness of Otto's backyard, stockaded by the shadowy shafts of the clubs, still breathless from my cab ride, still in a hurry to get home but afraid, too, of actually opening the breezeway door, that fuzzy image of Ray began to make fuzzy sense to me. As nice as he had been to my mother, as friendly as he had acted toward me, as essentially unobtrusive as he had remained when it came to my mother's life and my own, Ray was a killer. The word made me shudder.

I was onto something. It had to do with innocence. It had to do with the idea that innocence corrupts. It had to do with being a little boy, staying a little boy all your life, wanting to command a woman's slavish love—no matter what—wanting to overpower her with a little boy's body, turning instead to love of self because overpowering her was uncertain, secretly taboo. The desire to prove one's manliness persisted, but it was constantly thwarted by nagging self-doubt. So one turned it into impenetrable privacy. Unbreakable concentration. That was safer than beating up Flossie, though it turned out to be the same thing, didn't it? Yes, it did. Expecting good meals. Finding clean underwear in your drawer. Devoting yourself to work as though it were a god she had better believe in.

Being the aggressor at sex. Cheating. Lying. Giving clothes and food and shelter and pocket money in return for being left alone so you can continue providing clothes and food and shelter and pocket money and little else. Playing the part of husband. Playing the part of father. Are any of these proofs of manliness less devastating than the black uppercut to Flossie's jaw? Everything was more apparent when another man's action brought it into focus. That was why Ray had looked guilty in my hallucination. When he heard that my wife had killed the kids and herself, he searched what he knew of our lives for a reason, and suddenly everything was a reason: the older boy's problems, of course; my frequent business trips; life, in general, in the suburbs; the increasing frequency of our golf dates—every Sunday, and, lately, every other Saturday, too; my wife's half-joking complaints about how early I fell asleep each night; the fact that my wife had openly smoked pot at a family barbecue, and my double outrage that she smoked pot at all; the night Ray and my mother came for dinner and found the floors of our house littered with cookie crumbs and toys and my newspapers, my wife smiling through their embarrassment for her and schizophrenically stating that she had decided never to clean again, why bother?, schizophrenic because my wife had a reputation for neatness unsurpassed in both our families; the strange and insular way she had dealt with her mother's death, hardly talking about it at all, adamantly refusing to talk about it, in fact, whenever I was present, switching the subject like some deranged Tennessee Williams anti-heroine, a glazed expression falling over her face as suddenly she'd start talking about the weather or the TV show she wanted to watch later that evening (usually the shows she looked for were scheduled for one or two or even three in the morning, talk programs being a great favorite of hers, ones that pitted a caustic, conservative L.A. MC against passionate women who'd plead with society to forgive them their divorces, their child beatings, their abortions, homosexuality, mastectomies, their close encounters of all kinds—and old movies, too, little pictures made by big studios, featuring women who were slated for mass popularity and so were already sculpturing their one-dimensional screen images: ruthlessness, wickedness, idealism, ambition, sexiness, sweetness, bubbliness; I think she liked them because the old hairstyles and dress styles made her feel closer to her mother); the afternoon the two of us brawled while she was talking to Ray on the phone, what the fight was about I could no longer remember, but I had screamed loud enough for Ray to hear and nastily enough for him to remember; my absence during the birth of our first son; my insincere presence at the birth of our second son; the night Ray was hospitalized for the first time and my wife had to be dragged into his sickroom to pay her respects.

As I looked at our lives through Ray's eyes, the common denominator seemed always to be me. Whatever the dissatisfaction, the frightenedness, the solitude, the madness evinced by my wife's behavior, I was always the cause, screaming at her or ignoring her or sleeping or away on business or threatening or pushing or pulling.

He knew I had driven her to murder and suicide. He knew he was driving my mother to the same fate. It could not be otherwise. Men were men. Women were women. It was all instinctive. It was all innocent. No matter that my mother was strong enough or old enough or old-fashioned enough to expect less from life and so would not actually kill herself, Ray was just as guilty as I was. Just as guilty as that big black T-shirted pimp. In me he had seen the murderous instinct of every man, how we robbed our women of freedom by bullying them with our position and power. We gave them the care of their children as if that were crucial to the well-being and continuation of the species, and as if their embryonic bond somehow exclusively entitled them to this "privileged" role. But it was a trick. We just wanted them to take care of us until we were old enough to discard them.

My mind, shocked as it had been (might still be) had made me see Ray's guilt so I could recognize my own. Oh, Sweet Pea. Dear, dead Sweet Pea. I'm so sorry. Tell me, how can I make it up to you?

Otto's backyard seemed to light up, such was the brilliance of my understanding. In their own ways, the boys were just smaller versions of me. They demanded love. They demanded deaf, dumb, blind devotion. They were totally preoccupied with themselves as a means of overpowering their mother—and she took that to be the way of the world. They, we, forced her into an intolerable existence, for she had once, possibly, in college, in the halcyon days of our marriage (a marriage that could never have been considered on the rocks) she had once tasted a life of options, a life that might fulfill instead of fill her time, and then she had been robbed of self by her all-consuming boys. And what had we given her in return? Pain. More pain. Relentless pain. Intolerable pain.

Kill them. Kill the boys. One of them has problems anyway. Maybe he'll grow up and be a real killer. The other one is perfectly, wickedly normal. At only four, he is a master at manipulating his mother. Kill them. Don't let it happen again. Don't leave them to me. Kill them. It's the decent thing to do. It's the human thing to do. It's the only thing to do. And then the mere formality of suicide —after all, killing the possessors of your heart and soul *is* suicide.

But it might have been different. That's what tormented me. It might have been different, Sweet Pea.

I met a girl tonight. What a lovely child. She was all alone. She looked so provocative with her tight shirt and no bra and teenage ass. She was all alone, all by herself in that terrible neighborhood by the train station. And she asked me for a lift. She just came right out and asked me. She wasn't a bit afraid. Can you imagine? A young girl, alone, sexy, unafraid. Doesn't that prove that things can change? Look at the difference between you and your mother, how much more aggressive and unselfconscious and unafraid you are compared to her. It takes time. Maybe it skips a generation. But people can change. Even your mother was changing. Don't you remember what she said right before her surgery, when your father was downstairs grabbing a sandwich? "If I weren't so sick, I'd leave him," she said. Don't you remember? That's the terrible, terrible part of all this. You didn't have to kill them. You didn't have to kill yourself. If only I had met that girl three days ago. Just three lousy days, that's all.

•

How wonderful the human mind is. Mine was still trying to protect me, still trying to shift all blame onto my wife's frail shoulders. But, as I rose up out of Otto's patch like a scarecrow come suddenly to life, I knew what my clever mind was up to.

I took off my shoe and a half and tiptoed onto the breezeway, hoping not to be caught coming home so late and then realizing that that was exactly how my mind wanted me to feel. I dared to peek in through the windows of the back door. A room away I saw them. Not a limb had moved. Not an eyelash.

Our cat was on the kitchen table right next to the back door. She was pawing at the windowpane. She was meowing. She was hungry. I hushed her as I fumbled with my keys, but she meowed louder than ever when she heard the noise in the latch. Then, as I opened the door, she sprang to the floor and rubbed herself against my legs. In and out of each step I took she purred and rubbed, making it even more difficult for me to walk.

"Shhh."

Instead of allowing panic or shock or revulsion or sorrow at the closer and closer sight of the bodies, I forced myself to act calmly.

"Hey, monkey," I whispered, bending down directly over my youngest son. "Daddy's home."

He looked as if he were peacefully asleep. I touched his little arm. He was wearing underpants, nothing else. The front was yellow where my little boy had evidently peed. Remembering the shitballs I had cleaned up, I expected the backside to be a worse mess.

"Monkey, monkey, monkey," I whispered, "what are we going to do with you?"

I stood up, picking him up with me, hugging him to my chest. His head bobbed limply against my shoulder as I carried him upstairs to his room.

"Don't you want to know if I brought you something?"

He felt heavier than I remembered.

"Well, I did," I announced triumphantly. "I brought you me."

We entered his room.

"Shit."

His bed was stripped down to the plastic sheet on the bare mattress. I put him down into a little director's chair. The backrest had been taken off and put back on upside down, and so were the letters of his name, which had been cut out of felt and sewn on.

"You know," I said a bit defensively, searching his dresser for linens, "I was right there in the operating room when you popped out of Mommy. I saw you before she did. The doctor saw you first, but I was right in there, monkey. You were so red. And boy, were you ugly. I wouldn't say that if you didn't turn out so handsome."

I was there all right, but I had been more interested in the room itself with its amazing smallness and simplicity. It was another case of going behind the scenes and finding it not only glamorless, but basic, almost jerry-built, no fancy tricks at all. When my baby stuck a bit on the way out, the doctor used the same instrument that we used at home for grabbing cobs of corn out of boiling water, only the doctor's tongs were much larger. My biggest thrill was dressing up in a green doctor's gown and mask and paper booties. After my wife was rolled into the recovery room, I sauntered through the corridors still wearing my green mantle of respectability. In the cafeteria I was able to cut ahead in line to get a cup of coffee. Those who were waiting got back out of my way as if I were not only a doctor, but driving an ambulance as well.

"Listen," I said, giving up the search for a minute, "I don't want to lie. It's . . . there's . . . a father . . . a father just can't feel the same as a mother. I didn't see your brother until two days after he was born. You know what I thought when I looked at him for the first time? I thought: how do I know this is really my son? And with you, Jesus, I was right there, I was a couple of feet away, and still . . . there was no strong feeling of connection. I wish you knew what I was talking about."

I walked across the room to him, bent down onto one knee, picked his head up by the chin.

"I love you. Honest to God, I do love you. But I just . . . I never knew what to say to you. And I didn't worry about it because you were always so independent, so logical, so . . . grown-up. You walked on time and talked on time, you did everything that was expected of you. More. You know why I call you monkey? There was a famous experiment where they put a banana way up at the top of a cage and then they gave this monkey a stick and son-of-a-gun if he didn't figure out that he could get the banana down by using this stick. When you were real little, you always reminded me of that monkey the way you put two and two together, the way you figured things out, the way you experimented with everything. You know what you did one time when you were . . . you couldn't have been more than one-and-a-half . . . I don't know if you remember, but you fell down the last three steps going to the basement. You didn't really hurt yourself, you were just scared, and Mommy and I hugged you and kissed away the tears. But you know what you did? I was watching from the top of the stairs. You went right back down to those bottom three steps and you practiced falling. You figured out the best way to fall, how to land so it wouldn't hurt. That's why. That's why I never worried. That's why I waited. I figured I wouldn't have to wait too long until you were grown-up enough to talk to.

"All right," I said, with a sudden burst of energy and drama, "let's make up for lost time. Who says it's too late?"

I stood up and scanned the room for a prop, settling on the first thing that made any sense to me.

"Let's have a catch," I said enthusiastically, picking up a midget basketball. "Here's the thing, you've got to keep your eye on the ball. Don't worry about your hands, they'll do what they're supposed to. The important thing is never to take your eye off the ball."

I tossed it to my little boy; the ball hit the chrome arm of the chair and bounced almost right back to me.

"That was my fault. Bad throw," I apologized, scooping the ball back up into my hand.

I threw it again. This time the ball rebounded off his chest and rolled under his bed.

"You've got to keep your hands cupped, like this," I coached, placing his hands palms up in his lap. Then I retrieved the ball, cocked my arm, shouted "ready," and lobbed it at my target. The ball hit the inside of his forearm softly and rolled down into his waiting hands. It stayed.

I allowed myself a quick daydream in which my little boy stood dressed in Yankee pinstripes out in hallowed centerfield, the roar of the adoring crowd cascading down around his four-year-old body in its borrowed batboy's uniform, which was still floppy at the feet and shoulders. Even my daydreams, as outrageous as daydreams necessarily are, were tinged with a steely logic when my little boy was involved; how clearly I could hear him suggesting to the manager that the batboy's uniform would be the closest fit. And I could see, in one blurry margin of the dreamy screen, his mother sitting alone in a box near the dugout, frantically readying the clumsy sewing machine she inherited from her mother so that she could hem or dart or tuck while the teams changed sides.

I went back to the dresser to find a bed sheet and pillowcase. In one drawer was a stack of neatly folded shirts. Once they had belonged to my older son. I, too, belonged to my older son. He had received my first, sincere attempts at being a father, he had rejected them (through no fault of his own), and the four-year-old had had to settle for a secondhand relationship with his own father. It might have been different, of course, if the seven-year-old had ever responded. But he never did—not in a normal way. And so I was forced to overdramatize every little thing in hopes . . . in hopes. It had been difficult to work myself up again at the zoo or the circus or the ice revue or the playground or the park when it was the little one's turn. So difficult. Besides, he was always bright and inquisitive and self-reliant enough to experience life for himself.

I found a Walt Disney sheet full of daffy ducks and mice and pigs.

Who was I kidding, I thought, spreading the sheet over the bed. How logical and self-reliant could a four-year-old be? The truth unfurled in my brain like the folded sheet as I laid it out: I had insisted on the second child, forced his creation, conceived of him all by myself, even threatened to leave if my wife refused to go along with me. He was my brainchild. I prescribed him as therapy for the seven-year-old—that was why I wanted him, that was why I showed up at his birth—because he was my answer to our first son's problems. Conceived as a safeguard, a lifeguard, a guardian angel, how could I think of him as anything else? The seven-year-old, then only three, would learn from this little bundle of business. He'd watch his younger brother eat without playing with food, do homework without ripping up the worksheet, talk without drooling, walk without tripping, dress himself, wipe himself, tie his own shoelaces, brush his own teeth, blow his own nose, steer a toy car into a parking spot, swing a bat into a ball, socialize instead of terrorize—and he'd learn. When boys his own age laughed at our firstborn son, his younger brother would stand by him, find infinite patience, assimilate the big boy's problems into his own life, treat them as his crosses to bear and solve. And when Mommy and Daddy were too old or finally dead, he would look after his own flesh and blood, no questions asked.

That was why I had him and that was how I treated him—distantly, respectfully, as if he were a psychiatrist or priest.

Did he ever wonder, I wondered, tucking under the fourth corner of the sheet, why I made such a fuss over his brother's accomplishments and almost no fuss at all over his? Did he, aside from being able to do more than was expected, understand that I counted on his being able to understand more than was expected, as well? Even to the point of downplaying the facile sommersaults of his mind and body.

"I hope you understand," I whimpered, sitting down on the made bed, helplessly focussing my eyes on a mincing black duck.

It seemed that I had spent every occasion searching for an activity that the big boy excelled in and the little boy, because of the natural course of development, hadn't yet mastered; riding a two-wheeler, swimming, reading, joining the Cub Scouts. But even then, the little one always found a way to equalize abilities.

Once at a playground I watched the two of them try to seesaw together. Again and again the older boy's sixty pounds foiled the younger boy's twenty-five pounds. Still not discouraged, the younger boy found several large rocks and hauled them, one by one, over to his side of the seesaw. Eventually he persuaded his big brother to help, and when they had gathered enough rocks, the little one piled them onto the seesaw. The several rocks, the twenty-five pounds of logical genius, and the fact that I had already slotted the fulcrum as far as possible from my hopelessly outweighed son combined to work a miracle. Amazed, I watched the four-year-old slow the seven-year-old's rise and fall; he had even mastered the technique of increasing his existing weight by bearing down and leaning back. In a sense, I remembered thinking then and recalling now, the young one had recreated his older brother, for what was my problem child if not twenty-five pounds of potential normality and the rest rock—dense, dead, ageless, burdensome rock.

Instead of helping us cope, the little boy's nearly textbook infancy, toddler days, and budding boyhood only made us feel worse about the fraternal disparities, only pointed out pain, never joy. The plan had backfired.

When the little one uttered his first distinguishable, meaningful sound, instead of delight we were filled with a sorrowful remembrance of the older boy's gurgly "buh," his mystery pronouncement at one-and-a-half that illogically punctuated his speech forever after: I love you, Mommy-buh; buh, please; buh, I won't do it anymore; Is buh buh 'I Love Lucy' on now?" At my most optimistic I tried to believe that "buh" meant "but" and that my boy was so filled with a cosmic sense of doubt he could only hint at life's stupefying questions.

When the little one took his first steps, instead of filming the event, we mentally projected three-year-old footage of the older boy's finally, desperately (after parental hounding and badgering and threatening) taking a few faltering steps—but backwards—until he tripped on a tennis ball and justified his apprehension by thudding to the floor like a born cripple, a condition three different doctors assured us he did not suffer from. A year later, when he had learned to walk in the right direction, we showed him the movie of his first symbolic steps and got him to laugh by reversing the scene so it appeared he was walking forwards. If only all of life were that easy to reverse.

I imagined the clotted slashes along my wife's wrists sucking up spilled blood like vampire mouths, closing up neater than a surgeon's stitchwork, the color returning to my wife's face, a vivid boiling red from neckline to hairline, as she unsmothered the little boy's screams and unbanged the bigger boy's head into the edge of the dining room table.

Suddenly my surreal fantasy flew off the sprockets of my brain. Reality cut itself back into my inner vision. The image of my little boy. His chair. The ball. His upside-down name. The ducks. The mice. The plumped-up pillow. His little life orbited in my head, the things I'd seen but somehow missed: white shoes riveted to the ends of a corrective bar, red shoes free, brown shoes dancing; a crayon drawing of a face, my face; a house of blocks, a castle of sand; haircut, gum wad, bee sting; king of the jungle gym; knock knock, who's there, orange, orange who; bashful, skipping, singing voice; Christmas-birthday-Halloween wrapped in gold and green and blue; blue . . . ; cat scratch, head bump, knee scrape, bloody puffy lip; blue . . . ; fright of night; blue . . . blue lip, blue night . . . fright of night. I picked him up and embraced him and carried him to his bed and laid him down. With a trembling forefinger I brushed his lips. His mouth was slightly open.

"You were my brainchild. My brain."

I kissed his parted lips and shivered at the absent blast of hot breath.

"Your brother was my heart."

I lay down next to my little boy; his head was so close to my eyes I could not bring it into focus.

"You were born in the afternoon, and everything was fine. I spent the night with Mommy until the hospital made me go. She was asleep the last half hour, anyway. Then in the morning Mommy called me. She wasn't actually crying, but the sound of her trying not to was worse. She told me that a nurse had noticed that your lip was blue. Maybe there was nothing to worry about, but sometimes a blue lip means there is something wrong with the baby's heart. And your grandma had a bad heart, so we believed it."

I closed my eyes and tried to picture a bad heart. It was purple, the color of tainted meat; by the time the purple reached the lip, the bloodstream reclaimed the red, leaving only the faintest trace of blue.

"They were going to give you a special heart test with little electric wires when they could set up the equipment and when the right doctor was available. And meanwhile, that same day, I had to take your brother to a doctor, too—for a different kind of test. You would have loved his tests. One was closing your eyes and trying to make two fingers touch, one from each hand. Another one was stretching out your arms, closing yours eyes, and touching your nose with your finger. There was a walking test and a skipping test and a running test, and the doctor hit your brother with a special little hammer to see what different parts of his body would do. Those were all fun."

I propped myself up on one elbow and stared into my young son's face.

"But there was one test that wasn't fun. It didn't hurt, but your brother had to keep perfectly still the whole time. The doctor put paste all over your brother's head, all over his hair. Then he stuck wires to each little spot of paste and turned on the machine that the wires were connected to. Which is just what they were doing to your heart at probably that exact same minute."

My voice drifted on sighs. It was difficult to keep from talking to myself; it was hard not to muse.

"It was the worst day of my life. I was helpless. The happy lives of my sons were at the mercy of machines. The machines didn't actually do anything to you and your brother, they just recorded—

wrote down—what was going on in your heart and his brain; they just made a bunch of zigzaggy lines only the doctors could read."

I wished I could have switched the machines around. Or the boys. The big boy's heart always thumped like mad, and the little one's brain hummed along like clockwork. They were wired to the wrong damned machines.

"I called Mommy from the doctor's office, and she told me everything was okay. What a relief. But we had to wait a week to find out about your brother. That doctor only worked the machine. A different doctor had to read the zigzags."

The irony, of course, was that the younger boy loved to run and climb and use his poor heart to pump energy into his love of life, while the older boy would rather read or remember the words to songs or playact or fantasize or use his poor brain to sort TV data.

"Even though your test turned out okay, I always worried about you. At night, when I came up to make sure you were covered, I always looked at your lip for a trace of blue. I always sneaked my hand onto your chest to feel for a heartbeat when I hugged you or wrestled with you. I always wondered why your favorite color was blue."

I could not keep the folded blue spread, the blue squares in the plaid rug, the blue curtains, the blue toys, the blue finger painting hanging on the blue wallpaper from creeping into my peripheral vision.

It was blue and red outside. The sun was about to rise. I looked into my little boy's closed eyes and hated him for every time he made me punish him.

Once I made him go to bed without a night-light, using darkness—his worst fear—against him. But I forced myself to listen to his terrible howling until the desperate gurgling screams turned to sobs and the sobs turned to whimpers and the whimpers turned to fitful sighs of sleep.

I tried myself before the expressionless jury of one, but no longer did I believe in my own innocence. An automatic argument consisting of halfhearted accusations, hollow clichés, and desperate illogic trickled out of my mouth like a wounded man's blood.

"Sometimes you drove us crazy. Mommy especially."

Or were we crazy already?

"You were only doing what came naturally. But you could exasperate your mother like no one else. Not even your brother got to her the way you did."

She expected the big boy to disobey, to act up, to go against her. But she was never prepared when her perfect child, the one that looked and acted so much like her, was anything less than perfect.

"Oh, they were little things mostly—refusing to eat, spitting, talking back, messing up my important papers, turning your light on when you were supposed to be sleeping, dirtying your pants, taking whatever you wanted from the store without telling Mommy so she could pay for it or say no, playing with things that were dangerous like electric wires and cigarette lighters and pills from the medicine chest; remember that time Grandma was staying with us and you got into her suitcase and dumped out all her pills and we were sure you ate some because you were staggering around like a drunk all night? Maybe now those things don't sound like much, but they add up. One by one, little by little, they can drive a person crazy."

They can drive a parent to tyranny.

"If I told you once I told you a thousand times: you are not supposed to touch my papers."

They can drive a parent to temporary insanity.

"Your mother actually cried when you dirtied your pants. Maybe it was the idea that you weren't acting your age. Maybe it was the realization that one of her jobs in life was shoveling shit."

They can drive a parent to cruelty.

"Goddamnit, that time you wouldn't take a spoonful of honey, I swear I saw red. I'm still not sorry I dumped the whole jar over your head. It was supposed to be for your own good. You had a sore throat. No one was trying to poison you."

They can drive a parent to murder.

"Stop," I told myself, "stop playing the father." I stood up and smoothed the sheet where I had been lying. I straightened my little boy's legs, laying them next to each other. I put his arms at his sides.

The sun beat against the half-drawn shade. My heart beat against the silence in the room. I limped downstairs to the unfinished part of the basement. There was a sunlamp on a shelf above my workbench. I put the lamp under my arm and rummaged through the clutter on the workbench for an extension cord and multiple socket; I put these on the floor at the top of the basement stairs and hobbled purposefully throughout the first floor rooms unplugging and collecting several lamps. Finally I brought them all upstairs to my younger son's room. I sat on the floor beside his bed, fitting the male plugs into every available female socket and then plugging the whole business into the wall. The switchless sunlamp burst into an ultraviolet blaze of light, ticking as it did so, once, twice, intensifying with each lyrical tick.

I leaned back and grabbed hold of the little director's chair. I pulled it next to the bed and set the sunlamp on the seat.

"I want you to know that I am not all bad. I do remember the magic. I will always remember the magic."

I switched on a three-way lamp to the highest wattage; it hardly made a difference in the powerful light of the sunlamp.

"I will always remember your tiny hand wrapped around my two fingers."

I switched on the gooseneck lamp.

"I will always remember the million strung-together giggles whenever I threw you onto the couch or your bed or my bed and tickled your wriggling little body; how the giggles floated out of your mouth like tiny soap bubbles from a plastic blower and batted against my face and arms and hands—I swear I could feel them, I swear each one touched me and then quietly, quickly popped into thin air, leaving behind a moist and prickly presence that vanished all too soon."

I switched on the tiny piano light we used to illuminate the big boy's lessons.

"I will always remember the times you fell asleep in my arms, in my lap, all curled up and warm like you were attached to me, like I just hatched you, like you were one big sweet vital organ of mine venturing out of my body; I dared not move, dared not disturb your uneasy sleep for fear we'd be torn apart too suddenly. I'd hold my breath till I could synchronize it with yours."

I switched on the student lamp I had bought at auction; the shade was the truest, smoothest emerald green I could ever hope to see.

"I will always remember the sounds of your playing in another room or out back or by the edge of the lake; your singsong self-amusement, the thunk of blocks, the slap of plastic, the crazy tempo of a bouncing ball, the astonishingly sophisticated sound effects you provided for speeding cars, crashes, explosions, gunshots, boats, trains, growling animals, conquering superheroes, inhuman monsters. You had a noise for everything. You had a private language you made up as you went along to express emotions and events and creatures I never knew existed. Even now I half expect you to make a sound I have never heard before."

I switched on the floor lamp.

"I will always remember the way you ran and jumped and climbed and tumbled and sent yourself purposely sprawling. Sometimes I'd be at my desk and you'd fly by. Out of the corner of my eye I'd see you take a leaping flop onto the floor pillow in the den, and then, while you were still on the floor, I'd catch you spinning and rolling and making your feet go off in impossible directions, and I'd take a less-secret look when I knew you wouldn't notice so I could watch you pop up like one of those Popeye punching balloons you can't keep down."

I switched on the lamp that had been wired into a replica of a nineteenth-century book press.

"I will always remember you in the mornings when you were so incredibly wide awake, and at bedtime when you fought sleep right up to the very last second. Once I happened to be upstairs when you woke up—you were still in a crib then—and the second the sunlight hit your eyes you began babbling to Poochie Dog as if the entire night had only been a pause in the middle of your sentence."

I switched on the big brass table lamp and rotated the shade so the burn mark faded away from my little boy.

"I will always remember our good-nights, the whole routine, all the silly little improvisations that immediately became indispensable: searching high and low for you when I knew you were hiding under the covers; kissing your ears good night and then your eyes and then your nose and then your mouth, always in that precise order; getting up from your bedside while you were still hugging me around the neck so that inadvertently I'd pick you up along with me and never notice until two steps later so I could do a real good double take and throw you back where you belonged with a clown's melodramatic exasperation; ignoring your tiny footsteps until I got all the way downstairs and turned around, only to find you had followed me like a shadow, and then readying my fist to knock your head off, clenching it, blowing on it, aiming it, while you scampered up the stairs on all fours and finally disappeared for the night. I will never forget the sight of you going up the stairs, your hand-me-down pajamas tangled at your feet, your half-bare behind bobbing up and down, the melody of giggles accompanying your mad dash like a Spike Jones symphony.

"I will always remember the magic moments," I said, lifting the window shade and letting the risen sun pour into the shining room.

"It will never be night again," I said, making my way carefully through the light until I reached my little boy.

I kissed his ears. I kissed his eyes. I kissed his nose. I kissed his mouth. At the bottom of the stairs I turned around. But no one was there.

•

There was not literally a black hole in the side of my older boy's head. There was a dark, crushed gash which resembled a hole. It inspired a bizarre thought. My tendency towards bizarre thoughts (they were visions, not really thoughts, often grotesque, always stark and sorrowful) had been born along with my first child. Until then my head had always been filled with nothing stranger or stronger than the usual technicolor apprehensions everyone has about a life that is not yet predictable. The first of my "visions" had come in the form of a horrible nightmare barely two hours after my wife's mother had cried long-distance about the seventeen hours of labor her only daughter had just suffered. After hanging up the phone, I had had a cup of coffee, packed for the following morning's early plane home, tossed and turned in bed for half an hour, and then, probably no more than twenty minutes after finally falling asleep, I had envisioned my wife's swollen stomach being wrestled and boxed from within. Blind limbs fought against the human balloon, pushing, pulling, twisting, punching my wife's monstrous belly in all directions, stretching eerie silhouettes of themselves out of her shiny skin. It was as if a monster had gotten inside her, something terrible and fierce and dangerous—a crocodile with infantile arms and legs and a powerful, thrashing tail. A huge lump formed at her flattened navel and rolled like a treacherous wave toward the twilight between her thighs. Again and again these awful internal humps or waves materialized and rode themselves out. Finally the doctor was able to grab hold of the monster when a little piece of it wriggled through the flaming shutter that was my poor wife's reluctant vagina. Whatever it was, a foot, a finger, a head, a tail, the doctor gripped it with steel forceps and would not let go. The thing struggled in my wife's belly like a game fish, frantically flipping-flopping-somersaulting-squirming, not knowing which way led to life. Seventeen hours of touch and go. A seventeen-hour-long scream of agony pouring out of my wife's elastic mouth. Determinedly, the man in green tried to deliver the writhing creature. Delicately, he tried to ease each sharp horn along its armored spine through my wife's raw and bleeding opening.

When her wailing became my own, I woke up.

I had had that nightmare many times. For three years it had haunted me, even though every detail was always the same and the stark, grotesque images of the agonizing delivery had lost their ability to shock me awake. Just as I had learned to live with my son, I had learned to live with (or at least to sleep with) the bizarre visions he inspired. Then, when the second child came along, the nightmare disappeared. In its place, to fill the preternatural void, I began to have conscious visions, visions I could easily trace, as opposed to the mysteriously generated images in my nightmare. I could only guess at the source of those. But these daylit visions were a direct result of catching my older boy fantasizing, or stuttering, or sticking an inedible object into his hungry mouth, or unconsciously masturbating by pressing himself against a doorjamb, or nonchalantly wounding his little brother with a pinch a punch a push a poke, or "buh-buh-ing" hyperactively, or staring off into his own space in a manner cruelly reminiscent of ordinary human reflection, or sneezing on himself, or sifting through his farina for what? gold? poison? something only he could see? or lovingly choking the cat, or suddenly crying crocodile tears for no good reason, for no reason at all, or failing to fathom the simplest elements of logic such as one and one, the concept of consequence, Aesop, sleight of hand, or introducing himself to strangers, adult or peer, or conversing with inanimate objects, or destroying his own work or his brother's or mine, or dressing up in my wife's shoes and nightgowns, or any of the countless other "problems" which disconnected him from even the fringes of my understanding. Though he might have appeared eccentrically normal to an outsider, I was so overwhelmed by him, so consumed, so prejudicial, that virtually every move he made and every sound he uttered struck me as symptomatic of a constant, inscrutable mystery. The visions were simply my way of trying to understand.

As I stood in the living room staring at the black gash below the silken bangs of platinum, I imagined that the "hole" in my son's head was large enough for me to fit my own head through. I envisioned myself putting on his head like a deep-sea diver's helmet, adjusting it until my eyes saw out through his.

What must it be like to see life as he sees it?

Shattered.

Shattering.

A doctor had finally labeled it. I didn't remember the term. The minute I heard it I forgot it. Instead, I upset myself by remembering a neighborhood loony I had known when I was growing up. All the kids joked about him. We called him a jerk-off, an asshole, a maniac, an idiot, a buffoon; never once did we refer to him as that fellow with psycho-visual-motor dysfunction. Never once did we yell, "Hey you, the guy with soft signs of autism!" The closest we came to real terms was calling him a retard or cretin or moron, and they were not accurate. But they did just fine.

What the doctor's term meant was that my son did not see what I saw. Things moved, motioned to him, maybe even spoke to him, that to me were nothing more than paper towels, table legs, pictures, silverware, dried flowers, a pen, pajamas, farina, everything that hardly mattered in the presence of something which did actually move or speak.

In his funny way, my son delighted in a world the rest of us never even knew was there. Maybe he was a genius.

I had always hoped he was; the two extremes, genius and madness, somehow overlapped. But the older he grew, the less hopeful I became.

What must it have been like to see his mother's boiling face bearing down upon him? Did her nose fly off at him like a tomahawk?

Were her eyes scrambled and spinning like pinwheels? Did her tongue rear up and undulate like a dancer of death behind the footlights of her neat teeth?

She hated him. She honestly hated him. That is what he saw. And I loved him. But he never once saw that.

"Ouch!" The water was boiling hot. I was in the bathroom, filling the tub, still looking through my son's eyes.

My son. Not her son. Not our son. Not even now when at last she is closest to him.

He has always been more mine than hers. In looks. In temperament. In my nightmare.

What did the world look like to him the afternoon he disappeared from the backyard? My wife and I were playing Scrabble when somehow she sensed that it was too quiet outside. She ran out onto the breezeway and called him. She ran out onto the patio and called again. Before I knew what had happened, my wife had checked the pool and the neighboring yards and had raced to the front of the house as though she had heard the screech and scream of a terrible accident. On the way out to join her, I couldn't help but notice the Q on her rack of tiles. I paused to look at the board; every U had been played.

Meanwhile, my son was trying to sort out the world. The brain does that. It tries to make sense.

The sky flew down at him. Birds landed on his shoulders and chirruped secrets while they pecked at his ears. The ground moved without him, and it was a constant struggle to maintain his balance; he could not stop for a second to rest for fear the earth would spin out from under him. Other children playing on the block danced around him in a circle, taunting him with faces that looked like his mother's. But he loved their faces, the bulging eyes, the swollen lips, the livid skin; he reached out to palpate the disembodied bits of flesh and they disappeared in his grasp. Unreality was his reality. The curb was the great wall of China. Trees were the little stick-figure flowers he drew on the bottom of every drawing. Oscars peeked out of trash cans. Ronald McDonald danced down the lane. Monsters slithered in midair. The universe was constantly being created, constantly being torn apart, constantly being recreated, moving, spinning, flying, a light show, an hallucination, a torture.

The steam rising from the tub brought me to my senses. How I ached to really see what he saw through those eyes. Was it as shattered and shattering as I imagined?

When he wandered away that day, it was my wife who had panicked. She found him around the corner sitting on a lawn, pulling out clumps of grass and sod. First she hugged him and kissed him to see if he was whole. Next she began screaming at him about destroying other people's property. She forced his hands to replace the divots, and then dragged him back home where I was waiting, musing, hoping my wife would not trade in her useless Q, hoping that I wouldn't wind up with it and have to subtract its ten points from my total score.

I hadn't realized it then, but it was as clear now as the rising water in the tub: the parent who hated him was always there; the parent who loved him was always missing. Musing. Waiting. Waiting for news that the boy was a genius. Waiting for the world to recognize that his flesh and blood was the purest distillation of human spirit, human instinct, a miraculously constructed humanoid free of inhibitions, defense mechanisms, guilt, anguish, insecurity, tentativeness, morality; he loved everything, living or dead, animal, mineral, or vegetable, with exactly the same passion. All of his passion.

And my wife, despising every second of her confinement, was automatically, necessarily there; to sense that he had wandered and to find him; to shovel the food on his chin back into his mouth; to repeat a request or a reprimand a hundred times until finally she was forced to scream it; to scrub his itchy ass; to scotch-tape torn book pages, glue back the broken arms of plastic superheroes, sew ripped clothing, sweep up shattered glass, mop up spilled apple juice; to shake him awake for school—thank God for school; to turn on his TV shows—thank God for TV; to tuck him in at night— thank God for night; to teach him manners and right from wrong and true from false; to patch him up, take him to the doctor, the dentist, the emergency ward of the hospital; worst of all, to keep him company, to sit across from him at lunch and try to have a conversation, to try to extract from him even a sketchy report of what he did at school, to give in and play a game and have to break the rules to get the slightest bit of satisfaction, to try to chitchat with a neighbor without constant interruptions, to talk on the phone once, just once, without having to say "hold it" and then run to break up a fight or see what that noise was or yell, "I'm on the phone! Goddammit, I'm talking on the phone! Leave me alone!"

Did she hate him because she was always with him? Or was her hatred a secret hatred of herself? Of her failure. Of her inability to cope. Of her responsibility in creating this monstrous child.

"You are not a monster," I said to my son as I tried to pick him up. I could barely lift his dead weight. He was so big for his age.

"Mommy didn't think you were a monster either," I said, camouflaging a break in my voice by coughing. "She just thought we'd all be better off."

I had to drag him; I couldn't hold him. One of his untied shoes fell off. The mirrors in the bathroom were clouded with steam.

My wife saw him as a reflection of herself, even though he looked like me. Maybe it was her interest in biology. His problems were genetic. Maybe she held herself responsible because it took seventeen hours to deliver him. She was small. She disliked her body. Maybe she condemned the narrowness of her womb and her uterus and her vagina. A long delivery often resulted in "problems" for the baby. Maybe she felt she was atoning for his long birth by giving him a quick death.

Except she didn't kill him. I killed him. I killed them all. I had more love and understanding than anyone, but I kept it to myself. I hoarded it, glutted myself on it, preserved my own sanity instead of caring about theirs.

It was true. I had worked out a foolproof philosophy for myself. The philosophy was simple: my son was the personification of childhood. He was a concept. He was not necessarily real.

"All kids spill things," I would say as my wife mopped up for the tenth time that day.

He was impulse; he was sensuality. He had more taste buds than we did, all over his mouth, on his lips, chin, on the roof of his mouth, along the sides, under his tongue, even on his teeth; no wonder he crammed food in there, no wonder it hung out. Every bit of his skin was like the spongy blood-filled gland I asked my wife (and Deborah and Kathy and Rosemary and sometimes myself) to erect; no wonder he liked to be tickled, no wonder he rolled on the ground and stayed too long in his bath and slopped around in his own shit and picked his nose and sucked his thumb and played with his mashed potatoes. His eyes were not gray with newsprint; no wonder he saw deeper, darker, brighter, farther, no wonder he stared. Every stimulation was a new, exquisite experience that he forgot the moment it passed, so it was always fresh the next time. The world was always new. That was how I saw my son.

But my wife saw slovenliness, bad manners, inappropriate behavior, obsessiveness. While I shrugged things off, she worried about what society thought. How would he earn a living? Who would ever befriend him? Desperate as women were for a man, what woman in her right mind would trade her intimacies for his promises of security, loyalty, protection? It was even worse: how would he eat, sleep, move his bowels? Who but his mother would cook for him, wash his pee-stained sheets, swab his messy ass when it got so red and itchy he couldn't even fart without its hurting? Only a mother.

"You were not a curse," I said to my son, kneeling down beside his awkward body, which had crumpled up the fluffy yellow bath mat when I dragged him into the steamy room.

"If Mommy really thought you were a curse, why did she get so upset that time you wandered off on your own?"

Why did she? Surely she had secretly prayed that something beyond her control would remove the dagger from her heart. Unthinkable as it was to wish for it, if he vanished (not if he died, but if he just vanished into thin air, if he never was) at least the pain would run its course and life might become bearable again.

Why then, if she could not keep that wicked prayer from finding its way out of the dark side of her heart and up to the heavens, why did she do everything humanly possible to find him, including the inhuman way she sensed his disappearance in the first place? And why did the parent who really cared just sit there in a state of confusion for at least five minutes? And then, even after I had figured out what was happening, why did I just stroll out front and muse and wait? She could have pretended not to have "heard" his absence. I could have raced to the pool first, dredged it, dredged the whole damned neighborhood.

I began to undress my son. I loosened his belt, unsnapped his jeans, pulled down the zipper. I sat him up and pulled his polo shirt off over his head. One of his arms flopped against my face and hurt my eye. Was that why it teared?

In the papers it would say that one of the children had "problems." Maybe it would specify them. And the mere mention of his afflictions (thus ours) would justify the headline. To so many people it would explain my wife's acts of murder and suicide. Society could understand the pressure, the sadness, the despair, the hopelessness, the justifiable homicide such "problems" often caused. That was what made such problems even worse than they were, what they did to the rest of the family. Enough books and articles and telethons and made-for-TV movies had been provided to help the uncursed masses understand the pain. It was easy to forgive a mother who cried herself to sleep because children made fun of her son. It was easy to forgive a father whose head spun from doctor to doctor searching for a cure, searching for temporary relief, searching for an honest diagnosis, a dishonest prognosis.

It was easy.

Even I wanted to believe it.

I pulled off his shoe, socks, pants, underpants.

The saddest scenes stuck like tableaux in a wax museum. There are our best friends seated at our dinner table: Mark's forkful of shrimp and feta cheese is forever poised between his half-empty plate and his half-opened mouth; Miriam's young forehead is wrinkled up in an expression of sheepishness; she is speaking; the recording equipment is hidden; her guilty but necessary request is spliced so that the same words are repeated each time the loop of recording tape makes a revolution. "He's too unmanageable, he hits our Jason, he breaks toys; you know we love you, but it's best if we see each other without the children." "He's too unmanageable, he hits our Jason, he . . ."

There is the first psychologist: she is avoiding our eyes; her pen is suspended forever between her two forefingers. "It's too soon to tell, sometimes these things work themselves out, but you should not completely disregard the possibility that things will get worse; you may have to consider an institution some day." "It's too soon to tell, sometimes these things work themselves out, but . . ."

It is so easy to grope through the black maze of the wax museum and grab onto a brightly lit tableau when it comes along.

There, just around the memory's bend, a pack meeting: special den number five has just given its cheer—*We're Den Five, It's Great to Be Alive;* spastic arms and wobbly heads are impossibly still; disheveled uniforms sport hard-won badges and beads; the scoutmaster's cheeks are puffed to blow out the final candle; a blast of wind extinguishes the flame as his recording ends, then the trick candle lights itself again; the scoutmaster knows the cubs can't ever be trusted alone in the woods, that they can't start fires or put fires out, that they are Akela's lost tribe. "And may the light of scouting burn brightly in your hearts . . . Whooph!" "And may the light . . ."

There is the fourth psychologist: he will scratch his wild hair eternally; his wide-open, accusing eyes somehow contact my wife's and mine though we are sitting several feet apart; his other hand is frozen to the pencil which has just written the name of a book we should read. "I don't think there's a damned thing wrong with him. I think that you two are reading an awful lot into pretty typical behavior." "I don't think . . ."

Once you pay your admission, once you admit that you are the effect and he is the cause, the exhibits multiply. There is less darkness. The wax figures come at you like the crusades.

There he is destroying valuable research because he wants to see crazy Minnie Mouse; my secretary is trying to disentangle him from the miles of focus group interviews which were being rewound; the empty reels are still spinning on the elaborate tape recorder; over their constant hum I am constantly explaining that "this is where daddy works, don't touch." "Don't touch." "Don't touch."

There he is wired for an EEG; there he is deciphering inkblots; there are his parents afraid to talk about the future; there is his grandmother doing whatever he asks, spending hours with him up in his room, reading to him, singing songs with him, playing games that have no rules or losers, finally begging him not to sit on her lap, he's such a big boy now, her diseased heart has bloated her thighs and abdomen, the inside of her lap is purple; there is her funeral; there is his new madness, which is a form of mourning; he is spitting, he is getting angry, he is throwing things, he is wetting his bed, he is fighting at school, he is masquerading as Marie Osmond, her records are hopelessly scratched, one of them looks like someone took a bite out of it; and one exhibit is never lit, there is only the sound of his eerie falsetto, it is still a mystery, he wants to be a girl, he wants to be Cher, Lucy, Marie, Minnie Mouse, Daisy Duck, the girl who sells shampoo in the garden of earthly delights, he believes he is a girl, there is nothing sexual about it, he longs for shoulder-length hair and ruby lips, girls don't run and jump and climb and tumble and bat balls and all the other things he finds so difficult, is that why?

It's so easy for the reporter. So easy for the reader. So easy for the mother and father.

But it is a lie.

If he cut himself, would we hate him? If he broke his leg, would we shoot him? If the little one needed heart surgery, would we abandon him in the operating room?

No one will face the real reason. It is easier to blame God, society, doctors.

"But it is a lie," I said to my son. "The truth is that Mommy hated being a mother. The truth is I did not know how to be a father."

Saying those words aloud loosened a stoniness in my gut. Hard, sharp tears burned through my eyes. Suddenly I felt strong enough to lift the seven-year-old. I slid one arm under his back and the other one under his knees and stood straight up. He seemed to weigh nothing at all. Gently I lowered him into the steaming tub. The water buoyed him. But his head went under, and I had to pull him back so that his head leaned against the unsubmerged slope of porcelain at the foot of the tub.

"She did not like the time and space and energy it took. She resented having to spend her days and nights with you. Jesus, your problems should have made her love you more, not less. As for me . . ."

We were not gifted parents.

"The whole time, in seven years, I never ever gave you a bath."

Once, when my wife had a terrible cold, I came home from work and found her sitting at the dining room table crying. As soon as she saw me on the breezeway, she dried her eyes. But I knew she was crying.

"Why would I be crying," she said. "It's this damned cold. That's why my eyes are red. Everything's red."

I sat down and started going through the evening paper. My wife said that dinner would be ready in a half hour, first she had to give the kids a bath.

"Why don't you skip their baths, look at you, I bet you have a fever."

"They've got to have a bath, they're filthy. I took them to the playground this afternoon and they poured sand into their hair."

Other children played on the swings, slid down the sliding board, rode the merry-go-round. Ours poured sand in their hair. The big boy liked the way it felt. The little boy liked the big boy. My wife needed to clean away the evidence of their insufferable stupidity.

"I would have brought something home. You didn't have to make dinner."

My wife had to make dinner.

"It's just a stew. It'll be ready in a half hour."

Then she rounded the boys up for their bath. She had to drag them away from a "Brady Bunch" rerun. She had to tear the clothes off their suddenly playful bodies. She had to chase them upstairs, threatening, screaming, coughing, sneezing, her head probably pounding with fever.

While I read the paper I could hear violent splashing upstairs and my wife's angry screams to keep the goddamned water in the tub.

Why didn't I offer to give the bath? I told myself at the time that the baths were not as urgent as my wife thought. I told myself that it was more important for me to keep up with the latest news, the current fads, the movies, fashions, advertising trends, it was part of my job. The baths could wait. The children could wait. Everything could wait. Somehow everything got done without me anyway.

I don't know what my wife told herself. Maybe she thought the steam would help the congestion in her head and chest. Maybe she felt she had to keep some secret, sacred covenant and always see that the kids were taken care of, even at the expense of her own health. Of her own sanity.

She had to drag them and chase them up there, and then she had to drag them and chase them out. When she came downstairs her face was bright red. Lifeless strands of hair fell into her eyes.

She didn't bother to brush them away. She stooped slightly, giving in to the pressure in her chest. She set the table. She dished out the stew. I put the children to bed.

"But today I will give you your bath," I announced.

I kicked the door shut to keep out a draft.

"And after your bath . . ." I lost the soap and found it, producing the slippery bar like a rabbit from a hat, ". . . and after your bath, you do *not* have to go to sleep. You can stay up as late as you want. You can stay in the tub all night. The reason you always went to bed so early was because we thought you needed a lot of sleep. You always seemed to do better in school the next day when you had a good night's rest."

I lathered a wash cloth and lost my momentum immediately. I touched his toe with the soapy cloth, dabbing at the toe ineffectually, hypnotized by it, ashamed to look my son in the eye.

"We put you to sleep because we were afraid of you. We wanted to be rid of you. We were especially afraid at night, when you were sleepy and more subdued and liable to tell us things or do things that made us guilty and sad. You liked to snuggle. You liked to kiss. You liked to play the game where we had to guess how much you loved us. When your hair was washed and combed and almost dry, and your cheeks were rosy, and your teeth so shiny, and your pajamas soft and smelling like warm fresh laundry, when you hugged Mommy and begged me to let you stay up, you were an angel. The blond in your hair shone like a halo. There wasn't a thing wrong with you. The blankness seemed to disappear from your eyes. At those times, you were the most beautiful child imaginable. A blessing. A miracle. Don't you see," I finally looked at his wet face, "we were too tired, too skeptical, too afraid to love someone who only existed for five minutes each day."

Again I felt stronger. It might have been the buoyancy of the bathwater, but my littlest effort so easily moved various parts of my son's body. I washed his legs and noticed the usual black-and-blue marks a seven-year-old carries, but I knew he didn't get them by sliding into second base. I lathered his white stomach, and it made me think of a bird's smooth underbelly. In a circular motion, I rubbed lather all over his flawless chest.

Logically I should have washed between his legs right after his thighs and his behind. But the idea of touching him there made me squeamish. I was afraid I'd squeeze too hard. My own balls shrunk and I lost heart at the thought, but I did go back and soap between his spread legs, two fingers holding the cloth.

"I think I am most afraid of you when you pretend to be a girl. I don't understand," I confessed, dabbing in and around the joints and folds and creases. "I know it makes you happy. That and singing."

There is a part of the brain that is accelerated by some cases of neurological dysfunction. The other parts of the brain misfire, but this extraordinary part is able to perform miracles. It has to do with the memory bank and the computer. There have been reports of severely autistic children who can tell you—instantly—on what day of the week August 17, 1999, will fall. Or any other date, past or future. One of these kids—an Indian, I think—could multiply two eight-digit numbers in her head, but she couldn't put three words together in a sentence. These children have a mysterious gift. They border on genius. If they could talk, the *Iliad* and the *Odyssey* and Dante's *Inferno* would be like nursery rhymes to them. For those of them who can talk, those whose brains are not totally gripped by the vise of autism, the gift is greatly diluted. But it is still there. Such a child can memorize the alphabet at a suspiciously early age. He can take apart a lamp and put it back together again, without knowing how, without even knowing what he has accomplished. He can sing a song he has heard only once before. A song he may not even remember hearing at all. The signs are there. You just have to look a little harder for them.

"It doesn't bother me the way it's supposed to," I continued unburdening myself, able to wash his private parts less timidly the more frankly I spoke.

"Seeing you in your mother's nightgown and her feather slippers, or picturing you grown-up and in love with a man, I mean. It never disgusted me."

I pulled up his penis with my bare hand and bravely lathered underneath the tiny shaft.

"I never thought it would lead to that. The feeling you get from parading around in all of Mommy's soft, personal things is not a sexy feeling, is it? But it's not something you can control, either.

You don't decide to do it. I've watched you. It decides to come over you. Like a trance. Or a fit of laughter."

I stroked soap along his arm adoringly.

"You don't really make a very convincing girl, you know. When you dress up and pretend, you look like a bad actor. Your voice is all wrong. You're too big. I keep thinking of Milton Berle. He had a famous TV show. Everybody used to watch the "Milton Berle Show" on Tuesday nights. They say he sold a million sets. And on every show, every Tuesday night, he'd dress up like a girl. He'd put real heavy lipstick on his mouth, and wear thick, long eyelashes, and a wig, of course, and high heels—the works. But he was big, like you, and his voice was deep, and when he tried to walk with a wiggle, he'd always have a lot of trouble with the shoes, or with the hem of his floor-length gown. And the audience would laugh until tears rolled down their cheeks. People at home would choke on their food if they were eating dinner by the set. We'd all be laughing. The whole country. Even on Wednesday, just talking about it. And you could look at Milton Berle's face and see how much he loved to hear us all laugh. And you never thought for a single second that he was disgusting or sick. No. No, he was very happy. The way it makes you so happy. That and singing. When you're singing you're off in another world, too."

They can sing a song in perfect tune. The brain becomes a record player. The lyrics are enacted with the deepest feeling. Yet these mysteriously gifted children may not even understand what the lyrics are saying.

"Sometimes I try to imagine your world. I open its door just a crack. It's as far as I ever get. Still, it looks familiar. I think I see rose-colored walls, and the glow of soft mirrors, and a single bed that is warmed by a purple coverlet. Brown and pink encircle your bare feet. And on the wall a captain's wheel slowly steers you into the spotlight where you are about to sing. The words just come to you. Every next note of the melody is inevitable, it must follow, you don't know how you know it, you sense it, you feel it. And the audience loves you."

The room around us suddenly struck me as what it was—a bathroom. All four of us had shit or peed or thrown up in it. Guests had used it to do who knows what in. Strangers. An occasional repairman. A social worker connected with my son's school. The Avon Lady. The previous owners and their friends. The porcelain gleamed hard and cold as a public toilet. The tears on my cheeks were real; it wasn't steam that had turned back to water upon touching my cooler flesh.

"From the time you were born, all we ever did was try to stop you from being happy."

I watched the dirty water flow peacefully and then angrily down the drain. When it was gone, I stopped the drain again and turned on the hot water full blast. Clouds of nothing filled the room, softening the harshness. While the water filled the tub, I went into the bedroom to search my wife's dresser. In a bottom drawer, wedged between two wrinkled brown bags, I found the plastic container. Inside were blue and red beads filled with pretty liquid the consistency of honey.

"I gave these to her for her birthday, but she said she only has time to take showers now because she can't leave you two alone for more than five minutes," I explained, standing tall over the tub, watching the boiling rapids toss my son. The water level was now so high that it caught the back of his head; his blond hair fanned out darkly. My son's entire body was afloat, looking as it must have when he floated in his mother.

What long, strong, but unsure fingers—splash! A red bead just missed his bobbing hand.

The curve from his neck to shoulder, where I placed my hand so many times—splash! His gracefully weightless arms which could never swing a bat properly or fly a kite or support a pushup or embrace his father, arms which pounded frustration onto the keys of his piano but also floated as if in water whenever he sang—splash! The nose like mine, the teeth like mine, the ears which heard what the brain could not file for the future, the traitorous eyes which misled him into the sharp corners of tables, into holes and steps and stray toys and would have, sooner or later, I know it, misled him into the path of a speeding car—splash! Splash! Splash! Splash!

I touched the lips which would not learn to whistle.

"Like this," I instructed, pursing my lips, whistling one long, flat note.

The red and blue beads blossomed into a thousand bubbles. A sweet perfume rose like the steam. Clusters of delicate suds clung to my son's skin. The bubbles multiplied another thousand times; a soft white honeycomb filled the tub, obscuring the bather.

I turned off the water.

"Help me if you know the words."

I sat down next to the tub and began to sing.

"You better not shout, you better not cry, you better not pout, I'm tellin' you why—"

In the middle of each song I cried, and my crying carried the melody until I could recover. But I went on. I took a deep breath of perfumed air and sang every song he loved. I sang my heart out. And all the while, one by one, the tiny bubbles burst. There was no reason. No one pricked them. Their fragile lives simply ended. Slowly and surely the mountain of white grew smaller, revealing more and more of what lay hidden within.

"When you wish upon a star . . ."

I wished that somehow the silently bursting bubbles could take my son with them. But when the last of the bubbles disappeared, he was still there.

•

What was in those wrinkled paper bags hidden away in the back of my wife's dresser drawer?

I'd open them, but I couldn't stop looking at my son; I knew that if I took my eyes off him it would be for the last time. The little one was still in my eyes, but like the ghost of a blinding light after it has been turned off. I did not see him. I saw his memory.

I wanted to guess at the contents of the bags. That way I might control my memory of her. But that had been the problem all along, too much guesswork. From the very beginning each of us had guessed what the other one felt. And both of us were too sure of our keen understanding of human nature to ever second-guess ourselves. Even toward the end, when my wife had lost every bit of confidence in herself, she was confident in her analysis of my feelings. She was certain, for example, that her husband loathed the uncertainty which immobilized her. And, of course, she had been right.

I, too, had been right in thinking that she and the kids were on the road to ruin. I had only been wrong in believing the road led away from me.

Almost subconsciously, I was aware of the cat meowing and butting her head into my leg. The sound of the meowing was so distant that I mistrusted the little nuzzles against my pant leg, each of which were immediately followed by a cat's-length rub along my calf. Without looking, I noticed that I had left the door slightly open when I had returned from the bedroom with the beads of bubble bath my wife never found the time to enjoy.

I played what's-in-the-bag. After ruling out the possibility that the contents were not gifts for some future occasion, or odd buttons, or old check stubs, or the guarantees and warrantees of a household full of appliances, or no-longer-wearable garments still soft enough to become dustcloths, or any other disappointing collection of un-provocative, unevocative miscellanea, I tried to think of the parts of my wife's life that were worth saving. It was no surprise that I had to go back many, many years, which gratifyingly explained the worn, wrinkled condition of the brown bags. Although it was possi-ble that the bags were recent secrets and that frequent (even fanatic) handling could explain their condition, I felt I was on the right track to go back into her past.

Few husbands were as lucky as I was to have known their wives as children. It was fortunate not only at a moment like this—when the most important thing in my life was to reexamine hers—but hav-ing grown up with her also had added an extra dimension to our marriage, or at least a dimension other husbands and wives had to work long and hard for: we were like brother and sister. There was something between us that was so strong it could withstand any-thing, even falling out of love, should that have ever happened. While such a bond might make life generally less glamorous, it pre-vented any sharp decline in glamor from ruining the whole affair.

She had been almost abnormally happy in the beginning. If she wasn't smiling, she was giggling. If she wasn't giggling, she was belly-laughing. And if I hadn't thrown or caught the joke, it was the thought of sharing it with me as soon as possible that tickled her.

We each became the sibling we never had, without the rivalry. Together we cut up in school, predicted ironic fates for the class-mates we didn't like, provoked our parents and teachers to at least the point of a slow burn, and generally spent all our childish wit and energy making faces, mimicking distasteful body noises and taking off on the funny quirks of our elders and peers: Mrs. Klein's habit of hitching up her garter belt; Mr. Martino's tic; the ahead-of-schedule hair under Sharon Haskin's arms; Harvey Kern's fangs; Althea Washington's diction; Crazy Hymie's (the loony, the softly autistic, neurologically dysfunctioning Crazy Hymie) obsession with stationing himself at the busiest crosswalks to serve as everyone's school-guard when classes let out. (As unintentionally mean as our little jokes may have been, the principal of the school did us one better the day he presented Crazy Hymie with an honorary crossing guard's white belt and silver shield.)

There was really nothing worth saving from that period. We wrote each other no notes, gave each other no tokens of affection. We didn't know we would fall in love, so we couldn't have had the foresight to save movie stubs, soda fountain check receipts, the score sheet from a bowling date, or any of the other bits of a beginning that make the end so bittersweet.

Of course we had an idea that we were more than just friends. We had formed a society of two, and lavishly complimented each other by virtue of all the unlikeable people we kept out. But we never interpreted our relationship in romantic terms. Even when our classmates teased us about spending so much time together, we found the fault in them—jealousy—rather than in ourselves. But it was not jealousy of our relationship, we analyzed, it was jealousy of our individual superiority. Each of us had found the only other person worth finding at Milton Grammar School.

It wasn't until I accidentally glimpsed her breasts that romance occurred to either of us.

To celebrate her fourteenth birthday, we spent the day sunbathing on the roof of the apartment house she lived in. It was mid-August and the sun was so strong the ancient tar was tacky. The little extra effort it took to unstick our feet as we strolled the roof exaggerated the slowness of the day. After a ten-story-high look at the toy traffic to the south, the vast green and gray mold of the municipal park to the west, the other tacky black rooftops to the north, and New York's heart-blurred skyline to the east, we reclined on two aluminum and canvas lounging chairs.

I stripped down to my bathing suit, which I had worn beneath my dungarees. She removed her beach robe, revealing a bikini that was yellower than the sun. In the two years we had known each other, I had never really looked at my wife-to-be as a member of the opposite sex. But the blazing scantiness of the yellow and the shocking expanse of flesh leading to and from the yellow, opened a new eye, an eye I never knew I had, an eye that peered like a hunter's viewfinder through the tall blades of a hidden blind; I kept my two eyes pointed straight ahead, but still I was able to see her nearly naked body on the chair next to me.

We were very quiet. High school was less than a month away. Later I learned that my wife had just finished her first menstrual period. I was slightly embarrassed by my strands of a beard and the precursing shadow of a moustache, which were more in need of plucking than shaving and made me think for the first time that Harvey Kern's fangs were not his fault. We just lay there silently baking like gingerbread boy and girl dough on a charred cookie sheet.

"Happy birthday," I had said.

"I feel so old," she had answered.

And then it happened. She asked me to rub some tanning lotion onto her back. After staring at the sun through closed lids, her skin looked tan to me, but I took the plastic bottle and squeezed a worm of lotion onto my hand. It felt ice-cold. But I didn't mention it. Instead I aimed the nozzle directly at the small of her back and squeezed the bottle with sudden force. The ice-cold white goo shot out and hit her an inch or two above the bikini line. She jumped at least a foot in the air and shrieked at least an octave higher than I had ever heard her voice reach.

"You rat," she screamed at me, reaching behind her back to get rid of the icy worm.

I was so busy laughing at my prank I didn't see her pick up the plastic bottle until it was pointed at my face. I ducked out of harm's way and scampered out of my chair. She chased me until I realized I was stronger than she was. I let her come right up to me. Then I grabbed her wrists and forced the nozzle of the bottle back toward her. As I bent her arms back and up and over her head, the flimsy halter of her yellow bikini started to rise up over her even flimsier breasts. She had very little to offer in the way of resistance, and if it hadn't been for her protruding nipples, the halter might have slid up even quicker than it did. Out popped one blackish button of a nipple, and then the other. When I saw them, I squeezed the bottle involuntarily, and the goo spurted onto her hair.

Gallantly I pretended I hadn't seen her breasts. I doubled over in wild laughter to give her a chance to recover. I stayed doubled over, squeezing out every last fake guffaw I could, for at least a minute, or if it wasn't a minute—I've since learned how long a minute can last—I stayed down until I felt sure it was safe to look at her again. But when I did, when I dared to look at her, she hadn't moved a muscle. The yellow bra was up near her collar bone. The white goo was dripping off her hair onto her face. Her small but exquisite breasts stared back at me.

Maybe that yellow bikini or the bottle of suntan lotion was in one of those bags. They were, after all, the bow and arrow of our falling in love.

We did not embrace each other like movie stars would have in the same situation; we hadn't been to enough movies. My wife simply stood there for a moment or two, as I did, quietly, and then, covering herself up matter-of-factly, she said, "Would you like me to do your back now?" A week later, we made love for the first time.

"Do you suppose we always loved each other and didn't realize it?" she had asked, as I wondered exactly what to do next. Her parents had gone out, our pants were down, her legs were spread apart, Johnny Mathis was insisting that he'd be easy to find when love came looking for him, but I didn't find anything easy in the darkness of my wife-to-be's bedroom. Still, I have always counted that night as the first time. And years later, in a sentimental mood, she told me that she did, too. We never actually made love that night, but that first nearness, that first whispering, the first greedy kisses, even the unsynchronized wriggling of our hips and the melodramatic twining of our legs will always remain precious to me. It was the closest we ever came to making true love. The easier it got, the more difficult it became to appreciate how much we needed each other.

The cat was definitely in the bathroom with me. She wanted me to pay attention to her.

Good-bye, I thought to my son, and I looked down at the aggravated Siamese. She wanted me to do something, to go somewhere, to follow her like Gramps follows Lassie when Jeff is caught in quicksand or trapped in a cave or pinned by a fallen tree or fixed by the killer stare of a hungry bear. She walked out of the bathroom, backtracked a few steps, and waited. When I reached her, she repeated the same movements. By then we were near the end of the hallway leading into the dining room. The cat saw my wife slumped over, her arms pathetically embracing the space where the boys had been, and she pranced away from me to go sniff at the body. She sniffed it up and down, crept into the barely accessible lap, meowed, squeezed, sniffed, licked, nuzzled, and then left off abruptly to continue leading me into the kitchen.

The cat wanted food. I gave her some. Then she wanted to be alone. I let her.

It was too late to avoid my wife. Seeing her being sniffed by the cat had broken my resistance. My sorrow felt like a steel beam running from my throat through my heart to the bottom of my stomach. There was actually a pain. And I was afraid that if I looked inside her bags, that pain might never go away.

"We were so happy in those days," I said to her, still unable to stand too close to her body. The closer I got, the more intense the pain grew. But I was being drawn to her despite the pain. It was as if she were a magnet and her inescapable pull made the steel beam grind against my insides in a pointless effort to get out. If I had never grabbed her wrists that day on the roof, she might never have slashed them.

Unluckier couples fell in love and then had to work to like each other. But with us it had been just the opposite. We liked each other first, could not imagine a world without each other, in the same way one's family is a given; and then falling in love was not only easier, but it was more thrilling than having to work at blind acceptance.

From the moment I saw her breasts, I knew I loved her. And she, too, must have known it. Why else would she have stood there half-naked? The episode on the roof had marked an immense change in our lives together. Suddenly everything we said or did resonated with the poetry of being in love. If I put my hand on her shoulder to steady myself in a burst of laughter, my fingers tingled. As did her shoulder, I supposed. When I whispered some clever remark to her regarding Harvey Kern's fangs or Sharon Haskin's armpit, suddenly I smelled my wife-to-be's natural perfume, suddenly my hushed words transformed her ear into erogenous flesh eager to capture the everlasting echo of my breath, able to transport the echo to her memory so that alone at night she might call upon me like a genie to woo her to sleep. It was only a matter of time before we would admit to being in love. Only a week. And then all through high school, through college, through the early years of our marriage, through what had turned out to be the few middle years of our married life, we tried to perfect that love, relying always on our sibling beginnings to counteract that impossible task of ever achieving a true oneness.

In high school she was even happier than before. Her breasts blossomed slightly. She grew accustomed to her menstrual periods—as did I. We could not make love on any regular basis, too much depended on other people's plans—her parents, my mother and Ray's—but slowly and surely we were able to memorize every important inch of each other. She liked, for example, to be tickled behind her knees. It did not make her laugh. It made her weak. And then it made her eager between her legs. I'd marvel how a woman's lack of an honest-to-goodness sexual tool could suddenly come to life. The lifeless thicket would suddenly start to breathe. It would tremble. A dampness would untangle and slick and scent the hair. It smelled alive.

"But what could you have saved from those days?"

We used rubbers because I worked in a drugstore and could steal the best kind. But I always flushed them down the toilet. The wrappers, too. The boxes, when they were empty, I always tossed into the first sewer I came upon.

It wasn't until we turned seventeen and I got my driver's license that we began going places. That was when the silences began, too. When we first knew that we loved one another, we began to talk less. We had other things to do with our mouths. Less needed to be said out loud, and perhaps we were afraid that too much talk would jeopardize our happiness. Once I had a theory about the silences: it was intimacy that made us happy, so we had better hold back, we had better prolong intimacy by not making every intimate thing too easy to get at. Thus the silences. Of course, now I know that I was wrong. There was no running out of things to say, or feelings, or expressions of love. But we acted as if so many human qualities were in limited supply.

I noticed the silences when I noticed how much less silly we were together. We talked more about ourselves and less about our enemies. Maybe that was it. There were only two of us, there were millions of enemies when we were in high school: teachers, parents, senators, presidents, generals, businessmen, gossip columnists, game show hosts, rag sheet publishers, gushy singers, cardboard movie stars, anyone who skirted or perverted our idea of reality. We were beatniks, or what society called beatniks. We dressed in somber colors and saw the world in somber colors, too. We read poetry and tried to speak in poetry. A line at a time. With angst and tristesse.

The silences were never louder than when we drove somewhere together. We'd drive into Greenwich Village to "be," and we'd barely speak a word until we parked. It was as if we were holding our breaths underwater until we could emerge into the natural habitat of our destination. The romantic's rationalization has always been that two people in love do not even have to speak, need only feel the other's presence to be happy and as one. That has always been my rationalization.

"But it isn't really true, is it? Weren't there things we needed to tell each other? Isn't the truth of the matter simply that we were embarrassed? Isn't it true that you kept things to yourself because you were afraid I'd think you were stupid? And I would have had to say that you were stupid because I'd be embarrassed to admit that I felt the same way."

Maybe our old black turtlenecks and the dead microphone of a stick shift that stood between us in my first car were in her bags.

Whenever anyone asks how long I've been married, I always say that I took my wife to our high school prom. That satisfies the questioner. And it satisfies me. Our prom always seemed like the true starting point. It was a night of drunken disaster, and it set the tone for all the years that followed. We learned something about ourselves, and my wife was never as happy again, although I was buoyed by the experience for a long time without ever realizing it.

I had sneaked a pint of vodka into the party and liberally spiked our punch all through dinner and dancing. By door-prize time, we were numb. But I had called upon a man's reserve tank of sobriety because I was the driver for two other couples besides ourselves, and the plan was to drive into New York for Sammy Davis Jr.'s midnight show at the Copacabana and then to continue partying all night long. We had no real plan for after the Copa, just the emergency feeling that we could not waste a prom night by going home too early.

At the Copacabana I got even drunker. The double entendre humor of the warm-up comedian put me in a sexy mood, and I suggested driving to a motel after the show. But my wife-to-be was sobering up and starting to worry about my ability to drive anywhere.

"Lay down on this table, I'll show you what kind of condition I'm in," I remembered saying to her.

It was the first time I ever remembered those precise words. For twenty years I had only remembered saying something rough and tough and stupid. But now, for the first time, as I sat beside my wife tickling the back of one dead knee, the precise words revealed themselves like a code I had finally cracked.

"I was drunk. I didn't know what I was saying."

But when you are drunk you say what you feel, not what you know.

By Sammy Davis Jr.'s third encore, everything was a blur. My wife-to-be was a blur of color and smell and desirable flesh. I wanted to rip off my monkey suit and exhaust myself upon her body like Sammy Davis Jr. was exhausting himself on the roar of his audience's desire for more. He threw off his jacket, and I couldn't wait to do the same. He flung his tie into the crowd, and my wife-to-be caught it without trying; it landed on her bare shoulder, and she grabbed at it reflexively as though one of her spaghetti straps had snapped. I wanted to fling my tie at her. I wanted to unzip my pants and shove my enormous superiority complex into the blur.

We never got to a motel. We wound up in the emergency ward of a New Jersey hospital instead. At ninety miles an hour I had suddenly caught sight of a lead pipe sticking straight up out of the turnpike like the devil's periscope. To avoid it, I slammed on the brakes and swerved the car entirely around the pipe, coming to a dead stop heading north on the southbound lane of a superhighway. As late as it was, there was traffic, and I could see dozens of lights bearing down on us. I honked my horn because there was nothing else to do. All of the headlights, it seemed, shattered in my eyes.

There was a horrible screeching that came from everywhere at once: from the road, the sky, the lights, the steering wheel, my wife, myself, the back seat, everywhere. There were bits of glass in my mouth. I would taste them for months. The next thing I knew the lights had been pieced back together again into a dully glowing white circle on the ceiling of whiter tiles.

"You were all pretty lucky," someone said, his green head taking a bite out of the pie of light.

A few moments later I propped myself up on one elbow. We were in an emergency ward; I had not lost my ability to know where and who I was. A blood-spattered curtain enclosed my bed. But after checking my body, I was sure the blood belonged to some other prom casualty. As a matter of fact, I felt pretty good once I had come to my senses. Nothing was broken, nothing was even scratched. My leg felt sore, but not enough to stop me from getting to my feet.

I pulled back the curtain and smiled. There, lying peacefully on a thin mattress on a narrow table on wheels, was my wife-to-be. A sheet was drawn up to the top of her breasts. Her bare arms lay at her sides. A hospital gown just like mine was covering her shoulders.

I whispered her name and her eyes opened.

"You're all right," I said. "Look," I assured her, removing the sheet. She was all right. There was no blood, no bandages. She had been as lucky as her lover.

I pulled up her gown. She tried to say something and do something to help me, but she was too weak to speak or move her arms. I rubbed her between her legs and assumed her tears were of joy. My own sex organ prodded my gown.

No one came to interrupt. I made quiet love to her on the table. Halfway through, her eyes closed. The next day, in the backseat of her father's car, she refused to talk to me, acting remorseful for her parents' sake, but I knew the act was her way of giving me the silent treatment. She was angry with me, and I couldn't figure out why.

"Did they have to peel you off me?" she asked sarcastically over the telephone the following night.

Apparently she had not passed into a trance of love on the rolling table as I had thought. She had passed out.

"I didn't know you were unconscious," I argued. "I thought you were in ecstasy."

"My God! I was in shock. I couldn't move. All the wind got knocked out of me and wouldn't come back. I was laying there like a lousy piece of liver. You nearly killed us all."

"I guess I was in shock, too. I guess I didn't know what I was doing; the vodka, the music, the lights, the accident—I guess I was just glad to be alive. I wanted to celebrate. I thought you did, too."

"Well, I didn't."

"Well, I'm sorry."

I asked if I could see her that night.

"You'll see me in college."

Her corsage, Sammy Davis Jr.'s tie, broken headlamp glass, her hospital gown—what could be in those bags?

It had taken me all these years to realize the impact of that . . . impact. It made a long, depressing metaphor. My wife's life had been spent in the passenger seat. I drove; she sat there, worrying. We were both in the same car—our metaphoric universe—and at one point worlds collided. Both of us survived, but she was a slab of liver and I was a bloody butcher.

I couldn't think of a better example of rape than when the unwilling partner was unconscious as well. Neither could I think of a better example of man's unconsciousness.

All summer my wife brooded, refused my calls, wouldn't open my letters. But she saved the letters, of course, and we opened them all at once three years later, to celebrate our engagement. Very possibly my penned apologies, insincere as they were, had found their way into her crumpled brown bags.

Like twins who decide independently to stop wearing identical outfits, we created entirely different personalities for ourselves that summer. Abandoning our matching black beatnik outfits and outlooks, she spent all the gift money she had received for graduation on a brand-new college wardrobe of fall colors and fabrics, while I saved a fortune by deciding that all I needed were the two durable work shirts and the stiff Levi's I had purchased in an army and navy store as the uniform for both my summer construction job and for my emerging life thereafter as a rugged, survival-prone man of the world.

Although I hadn't ever mentioned our lovemaking to a single soul in high school, on the construction site I found myself bragging how I'd shot my load into the jaws of death in the emergency ward of the hospital following a catastrophic accident. It was the only he-manly exploit I had had, and so I made a great many acquaintances on the job in order not to bore one or two co-workers with the same story day after day. I loved telling it. I loved embellishing it. I wished I had lost a few toes or fingers or a whole arm or at least come away with an ugly scar to give my jaws-of-death tale more teeth. I wished, too, that my wife-to-be would speak to me when I phoned or would please answer my pathetic letters.

When I wrote them, the letters were not sincere. They were something I had to do in order to continue our relationship. To that end they had been sincere. But I had not been "honestly ashamed of myself." I had not been "crying myself to sleep every night" since my "temporary insanity" caused me to "stupidly attack, rape, violate, and degrade the only woman I will ever truly love."

And yet, for her entire life, my wife remained the only woman I ever truly loved. And those letters said everything I felt right now—now that it was too late, now that my wife had left me for the second and last time.

It wasn't really fair to say that she had left me that summer. Rather she left the part of herself that had been tied to me. It was not me she hated. It was what I made her hate about herself that upset her. She didn't want to feel as though the wind had been knocked out of her, and she wanted to find out if other men (men who would love her first and like her later—if ever), if they, too, would make her feel windless. Was it only me, or was windlessness the fate of every seventeen-year-old female regardless of whom she loved?

Her research lasted for three years, although it began to peter out in the middle of the second year when she had gone back to dating and sleeping with me fifty percent of the time she spent dating anyone. Whether or not she could foresee the windlessness she was trying to avoid before she had to sleep with the other men in her life, I still did not know for sure. But I always suspected the best: that she had not been intimate, that her lungs began collapsing as soon as the least breath of male musk got near them, that life for a woman was one long continuous gasp. The image of her readying herself in the labor room for our second son's birth confirmed my suspicion: pale and flat as a woolen garment spread to dry, she panted according to my signals. I'd point, she'd pant. That was the natural method. A father felt closer to the creation of life when he could be blissfully obvious about cuing the moaning of his woman. The cue was designed to make his laboring mate relax the pain. So, in reality, the pain of windlessness was woman's way of relaxing the worse pain of simply being a woman. It had taken her three years to face that fact. Twenty years to do something about it.

I unbent my crumpled wife and gently eased her down onto the dining room floor. One eye was open. Otherwise she looked as if she were asleep. The cat heard the nearly soundless noise of my wife's head touching down onto the deep pile carpet. She scampered back in from the kitchen, froze like a stopped movie, and then slunk warily up to my wife's body. The cat sniffed at the air, at the scent the air kept alive, at my wife's feet, up along her calves and thighs. She stuck her twitching nose into my wife's crotch for further reassurance. Satisfied that the still body was not the enemy, that it would remain still for a while, the cat climbed into the long and cozy gutter formed between my wife's aligned legs and settled in like a sphinx. The two of them looked like a single being, thighs joined to underbelly, and I thought that this—a drowsy hank of soft mauve fur that will only purr or spit—this is all of her that remains alive after all our years together.

The silences, the windlessness, it sounded so melodramatic. But those three years had passed as unremarkably as the days of the week. That's what made it so depressing now: to think, so much evil had been done at a time when so little seemed to have been happening at all. Apparently evil happens in retrospect, or else we'd be wise enough to avoid it. Wasn't that happening to me now? Weren't the evil things I'd done to my wife and children springing out from the darkness like hidden guests at my surprise party?

My wife and I had not raged at one another that summer. Even the scenes of our ride home from the hospital and the following night's telephone conversation had called for disappointed but decorous attitudes on the parts of the leading players. It was almost as if the script of our lives had already been written; we knew we'd wind up together, but first there had to be conflict. In my case, it was simply a matter of passing time until the inevitability of the plot reunited me with the object of my desire. In my wife's case, she had to carry the drama, she had the bigger and tougher role. She represented the struggle. I represented doom.

The first of her other men had been Harvey Kern. He had always been in puppy love with my wife-to-be, but self-consciousness about his fangs prevented him from ever speaking to her frankly. If he tried, the words seemed to catch on his pointy canines and come out shredded with embarrassment. But Harvey Kern had paid a good share of his graduation money to a dentist who, by filing down the fangs, simultaneously erected a magnificent ego. The new Harvey Kern felt handsome and glib enough to ask my wife to a movie before the Novocain wore off.

When I found out, I took it calmly. My keen understanding of human nature reassured me. My wife was simply fishing as far away as possible from the only spot she knew. No one could be more different from me than Harvey Kern. Thus no one could make my wife-to-be feel more different about herself. My keen understanding of human nature told me not to worry, that she'd feel me tugging on her line even as Harvey Kern leaped high out of the water sleek and proud as a performing porpoise. But now I saw things differently: in my present analysis of what my wife had been trying to accomplish by dating Harvey Kern, she was swimming instead of fishing. Her arms cut in and out of the water slowly, as though she were whipping someone who deserved it and she wanted each lash to be a distinct, tortuously measured lesson in itself. The ocean filled my mind, and my wife was approaching the very middle of it. But she was losing her breath. Each stroke sucked another bit of precious wind from her exhausted lungs. Finally, when she was exactly halfway across the ocean, she had to admit to herself that she did not have the stamina to go on. I was not worth it. No suggestion of a distant shore, no matter how romantic or safe it promised to be, could inspire the strength and breath necessary to cross the remaining half of the ocean. And so, accepting Harvey Kern's toothsome invitation, she turned around and began the equally impossible swim back home.

Harvey Kern had winded her in a different way, but he had

winded her. Newfound confidence notwithstanding, when my wife accepted his invitation he reverted immediately to his old self. Phantom fangs chewed up his appreciation and let only mutilated bits and pieces of his plans for Saturday night escape. He meant he would pick up my wife at eight for the first show, but he said something that sounded to her like "Eat first," and so when he showed up at the door, she was in the middle of a worrisomely garlicky meat loaf. This—and all the other "other men" details she was willing to tell—my wife had joked about when finally she realized it might as well be me who winded her: she swore Harvey Kern's fangs regenerated before her very eyes as he stood in her doorway shuffling his feet and wishing he were dead. What else could my wife's mother do except ask the misunderstood caller to help himself to the one last slab of meat while her daughter hurried to get herself dressed for the date?

It was the beginning of the end for Harvey Kern. Through the one month their relationship managed to survive, he dug a deeper and deeper hole of humility. Wanting to make up for the misunderstanding, he created a series of stupid atonements, one spawning the next, until finally my wife-to-be could not breathe. For their second date, which she agreed to out of pity and in order to give her new life some momentum, my wife received a single-spaced typewritten letter reminding her when to be ready, what to wear, whether or not to eat, et cetera, et cetera. When her reaction was cool (a paper-thin John Alden, she called him, the night I got to connect the missing links of her life) he launched into a new and even stupider strategy. He would call her twice a night, as if by constant practice his mouth would stop sabotaging his heart.

There were other things, too; I've forgotten most of them, but for a solid month Harvey Kern knocked the wind out of my wife with one suffocating kindness after another. Then he did an about-face. Their last night together had been the last straw.

He took her dancing and held her too close, apparently having decided that his careful worship of my wife-to-be at last deserved the reward of her bodily affection. But my wife was not attracted to Harvey Kern. She was too busy floundering in the middle of the great ocean, reluctantly starting to realize that all shores were equidistant. Each slow dance was an awkward wrestling match; he pulled her closer, she pushed him away, his arm encircled her back, her hand loosened his hold, he pawed at her hips and thighs, she broke away—in tempo, as though it were a dance break—and then twirled back for another round.

Because it was easier to let the outside world solve her problems, she agreed to dance with a stranger while Harvey was at the punch bowl. What followed could not possibly have been as horrible as my wife's description of it.

"We were dancing," she had told me, her eyes widening as if she were telling a ghost story to the kids, "when all of a sudden this mad dog leaped at my partner's neck. The dog was snarling and sort of hiccuping and its whole body was tense—as if it were doing a shit on the sidewalk. The dog's ugly yellow teeth sank into the poor guy's neck as if it were butter, and the two of them fell down onto the dance floor, the dog on top, the dog jumping from one side of the guy's neck to the other but never loosening its jaws. I was too shocked to even scream. A few of the people near the attack stopped dancing, but the band went on playing. Someone tried to pull the mad dog off, but he couldn't. The dog let go of my partner, snapped at the fellow who was trying to break up the fight, tore an instantly bloody gash in his hand, and bit back into the wounded neck of its original victim before anyone had a chance to recover or get away or even know what had happened."

The mad dog had been Harvey Kern, of course. When he saw the love of his life dance off with someone else, an insane anger seized him, and he attacked the stranger viciously, though surely not so viciously as my wife had remembered. She ran out of the dance hall still too winded to speak, and never saw Harvey Kern again. He called her, but she wouldn't speak to him. He wrote her, but she burned his unopened letters. He parked outside her building one night for several hours, baying at the moon of her bedroom window, I imagined, but my wife hadn't been at home. She assumed it had been Harvey, based on her mother's sketchy description of the nervously pacing young man who would call my wife's name and then, when her mother opened the window to see who it was, would stammer and sort of hiccup and finally skulk back down the block, his tail between his legs.

If Harvey Kern was in any way memorialized by the contents of these bags, I'd rip them to shreds. But the sailor was a different story.

It was entirely possible that the sailor had really meant something to her. The college men who followed were surely not important. The night she told me about her other men, she dismissed them each with a sentence or two that somehow reflected the short, wry dismissals they had probably received.

Bruce Mathias, the plug-ugly middle linebacker on our dismal college eleven, had only wanted to scrimmage with my wife in the locker room, where he no doubt felt like king of a dank, rank castle. Whenever she refused, he'd punch a hole the size of his fist through whatever wall was handy. Finally he broke four fingers in a fit of rejection, was lost for the rest of the season, lost his football scholarship, and joined the Coast Guard where, my wife had mused, he'd have the opportunity to sink an entire ship if some leggy mate turned him down.

Adrian Garfinkle, the pimply professorial student of unfathomable mathematical theories, had been more interested in a Phi Beta Kappa key than in the key to my wife-to-be's heart. He had taken her out only once, to a foreign film about life, death, love, longing, truth, justice, God, and the downfall of western civilization, and the first thing he had said upon walking out of the theatre was that, in theory, one could fit four hundred and eighty-two radial tires in the space of one standard-sized movie screen.

Leon Bloom, her lisping thespian, had lasted slightly longer. He represented my wife's first real contact with amateur theatrics. At seventeen Leon already had the puffy face and bloated body of a character actor and saw my wife as a nubile ingenue. But she closed his show when he insisted that she could only overcome her innate fear of standing emotionally naked in front of an audience by standing physically naked in front of him—though he promised not to touch.

The handsomest of her other men had been John Tyler, who sounded like a former president and acted like a future one—of a major corporation. He was studying economics, marketing, and business administration, but that was just because he had to have those courses on his résumé. Clearly he was planning to rely entirely on his good looks, easy charm, and opportunistic sixth sense to get him where he wanted to go. She might have gone along for the ride, but his Maserati of an ego had only a single bucket seat. When she purposely stood him up one night and he failed to even notice it, my wife-to-be simply disappeared from John Tyler's master plan like an unsatisfactory secretary.

At a civil rights demonstration, she had met Earl Jenkins, whom I had known from a psychology class. Earl Jenkins wanted to feel happier about being a Negro and had gone to the demonstration for the same reason the cowardly lion had gone to Oz—to get some courage. And like that imperious wizard, the demonstration succeeded by virtue of its self-evident good sense. Black was beautiful if you simply said that it was. But, of course, that theory and their sinfully exciting mixed feelings for one another broke down as soon as my wife and Earl left the wonderful world of Osgood Hall where they had attended three learn-ins and a B. B. King concert.

I sat back against the wall, lit a cigarette, and knew in my heart that the contents of the bags were more important than these ephemeral suitors. Nor would she have saved the rat's eye the future Dr. Robert Silvera had carefully strung on a length of dental floss and presented to my wife as a "gift more meaningful than a diamond, for a diamond is forever, but sight is mortal." Nor the tiny American flag that the White Pig—that was the only name he would admit to—had plucked from the handlebars of his ferocious Harley and demanded that she wave whenever she felt in the mood for a sexual wheelie or two. She would not have saved the White Pig's flag or the pre-med's eye or a wiry hair from Earl Jenkin's cowardly mane or anything else from those first three years of self-enforced oat-sowing. But the night we spent the whole night long laughing about her dates, she never mentioned the sailor. Nor did I.

"He made me very jealous," I said to my dead wife. "The worst weekend of my life. I only thought about that handsome sonofabitch making love to you. Experienced love. Doing things he'd learned in Holland and Paris and San Diego. I think I was more afraid you'd fall in love with his tricks than with him. I knew I was probably smarter than he was and that you thought I was attractive, but how could I compete with his experience, his technique?"

I stretched out my leg and touched my bare toes to her bare toes.

"I never loved you more than I did that weekend. Never."

I looked at the ten toes, the alive five trying to infuse life into their smaller counterparts.

"And now. Now, too, I love you the way I did when I thought you would go down to the lake and never come back."

But she did come back. Her girlfriends, what few she kept, began to get married. One by one they fell to the scourge of the late teens and early twenties. In those days, if you weren't married by twenty-five, you might never get the chance. In those days, a woman's future depended upon finding and catching a man with a future. While the universe looked like a seamless, endless ridge of towering mountains to a man, like three hundred and sixty degrees of ocean, like boundless skies and countless stars and a bottomless chest of chunky treasure, to a woman the universe was reduced to a reflection of the universe in the eye of a single man.

Jill Farkus got married, and although the groom had the look and smell of failure about him, my wife thought Jill was making the right decision, if only to turn the laughable Farkus into a more respectable Johanson. That's what Jill had always needed, more self-respect.

Eileen Miller married an older man and honeymooned in Spain where her moustache, my wife joked, would look less conspicuous.

Harriet Englehart took her vows in a ballroom of the Plaza Hotel, just five stories below—my wife-to-be felt it necessary to quip—the scene of Harriet's month-long courtship.

One by one they fell, like autumn leaves. You could see them snap off in the sudden, gruff wind and flutter giddily down into a life of mulch; if you watched long enough you could see them turn brittle and then mealy and then disappear as they spent the rest of their lives trying to protect and nourish their men and their children.

My wife had joked and criticized in her season of marriage, but she was not unsympathetic. What else was there for these otherwise futureless women? What else was there for her, as well?

She had forgiven me enough to talk to me again by the end of that summer. We saw each other at the terrible camp weekend, and we had enrolled in a few of the same classes. Though she dated like a terminal patient sucks in air, as often and appreciatively as possible, she would not date me.

"I need some time to think," she'd said.

"I have to find out what my life is all about," she'd said.

"We've spent almost our whole lives together," she'd said, "I know you. I'll always know you, but now I want to know other men. I owe it to myself."

And so she floundered in her sea. Until Margaret Hennesy invited us to honor and usher her into holy matrimony.

"Dear Margaret," I had written to her, "of course I will be there. I'm so happy for you I'm shaking."

Margaret was lucky to be alive. She had always talked about suicide the way other young girls talked about wanting to be a nurse. It was something she'd do when she was qualified. And qualification had meant painting a twentieth century masterpiece and having it laughed at or slashed by the offended citizenry. As positive as she was of her worth, she was even surer that no one in the world would give a dime for her life. Her paintings—abysmal expressions of the blackest moods—were the only things that kept her going. I always suspected that if she ever painted something she truly believed to be a masterpiece, they'd find her in a pool of blood before her gray and black acrylics had a chance to dry.

My wife and I had loved Margaret because she was a beatnik without having to act like one. She really was obsessed with death; her talent really did splatter against the canvas like brains squashed under the breakneck wheels of America on the move.

When all at once we outgrew our adolescent infatuation with the beat generation, we stopped seeing Margaret Hennesy, although we did not stop loving her unshakable commitment to life and death. The grapevine had kept us informed: she had gone to Yugoslavia for the summer, where rumor had it she tried to paint the copper-colored tin roof of her bungalow midnight black and was arrested for her trouble; at the start of the school year, she was back in America again, having been released through considerable and intrigue-filled diplomatic efforts, and she began a disastrous two months at the Rhode Island School of Design; after a teacher had ridiculed one of her paintings for its failure to ennoble the human spirit, Margaret Hennesy, mistaking that painting for the masterpiece she was never to create, shot herself in the stomach.

We hoped she would die, but she survived. For two years she

convalesced at a mental institution in Buffalo, and we assumed that there she'd stay until the grapevine strangled us in our old age with news that rheumatism or hardening of the arteries or some such unworthy, but ennobling, force had finally spirited Margaret Hennesy away. No wonder I shook when I received an invitation to her wedding.

"Let's go together," I had asked my wife-to-be.

For two weeks we tried to figure out who the groom was. Her psychiatrist, perhaps. The diplomat, perhaps. A connoisseur of art who stumbled upon her genius while visiting one of his tortured artists at the sanitarium, was my best guess. The teacher who had ridiculed her at the Rhode Island School of Design, my wife suggested, delighting in an irony no one would appreciate more than Margaret herself. If we had spent the rest of our lives guessing, we would never have come up with Alan Kovac, a thirty-five-year-old parking lot attendant from Niagara Falls.

The remedial patients were occasionally treated to day trips. On one such outing to the awesome falls, Margaret Hennesy met and fell in love with Alan Kovac. Her yellow bus had been unsuccessfully trying to negotiate a U-turn in the parking lot when love struck in a skidding Chevy.

"It was like shock therapy," Margaret would later say. "I hit my head, and suddenly I couldn't remember anything bad. Alan pulled us all out of the bus, one by one, many of us resisting, because he was afraid there'd be an explosion. You know what he said to me as he pulled me to safety? He said, 'What are you doing here? You don't belong with these loonies.'"

During the next month, Alan Kovac came to visit Margaret every day. His cheerful, lustful, loving presence had a miraculous effect. Even the psychiatrist had to admit it was a miracle, "although a miracle not without psychiatric precedent, of that you can be certain."

In another month, Margaret Hennesy was released to the everlasting, worshipful custody of Alan Kovac. In one more month, they would be married.

A week before the wedding, my wife and Margaret spent all their free time together. They shopped for a trousseau, looked for an apartment, combed the classified for a parking lot attendant's job, and told each other their innermost feelings.

I know Margaret Hennesy's innermost feelings because you re-told them to me, I thought, switching my eyes from the ten touching toes to my dead wife's one-eyed slumber, but I never knew your innermost feelings, did I? Unless I was supposed to make a connection between what you felt and the things you chose to tell me that other people felt. Is that how it worked? Should I have assumed that it was actually you talking through Margaret who was talking through you? But you had no ugly self-inflicted scar where a bullet had torn through your stomach. You were never afraid that the old sickness would return and Alan's blond hair would look gray and his blue eyes would turn black and the copper-colored roof of your love nest would cave in on us just as we were about to reconsummate our marriage. You never wondered why I loved you, what I could possibly find in you worth loving, why I didn't go back home to Niagara Falls and find myself a sane woman, a woman whose lungs were bursting with fresh air, a woman whose life didn't depend on Alan Kovac's reckless driving.

The suicide attempt had prevented Margaret Hennesy from ever having children. But they adopted a Korean war orphan. And they all lived happily ever after. And my wife, who had comforted the bride-to-be for a solid week and convinced Margaret and herself at the same time that marriage was perhaps the only thing worth living for, my wife lay before me like a bit of early Hennesy irony, like a grotesque sketch for a masterpiece sprung from the aching imagination of my lame foot.

"Tell me."

I yanked my foot away.

"Tell me your innermost feelings."

But the slashes across her wrists told me everything there was to tell.

As Alan Kovac lifted Margaret Hennesy's veil to kiss her, my wife looked across the altar at me. Later she danced with me, close beyond Harvey Kern's most rabid dream.

"I still want to date other people, but I will date you, too," she whispered into my ear during an unforgettable swell in the three piece band's tinny rendition of "Chances Are."

No more was mentioned about the episode in the emergency ward, but it was there. Even I felt it. When we had the chance to

make love, a vague pressure like the distant threat of rain made us
keep looking up over each other's shoulders to see if the sky was
still bright. And still, beneath it all, we remained as unquestioningly
close as brother and sister, asking for no apologies, no excuses, no
explanations beyond the matter-of-fact bond neither of us could ever
sever if we wanted to.

Despite falling in and out and back in love, we never stopped
liking each other. I had made a list once, as a birthday card, of all
the things about her that I liked. That I would like even if we were
not in love. I remembered every word.

"I like your hands." But I could not look at them now.

"I like your smile. I like your crazy jokes. I like your white mo-
hair sweater. I like your tiny handwriting. I like the way you say the
word 'blouse' as though it had a Z in it. I like your walk, it's so
brisk and utilitarian. I like your taste in movies, records, books. I like
the way you don't make up just any words if you forget the real ones
to a song you're singing. I like the way you never have to search
for anything in your pocketbook. I like the fact that bad comedians
can't make you laugh. I like your hair and the way it curls. I like
that you write poems and refuse to show them to anyone, including
me. I like the fact that the physical structure of your face prevents
you from ever frowning. While I'm in that area, I like your lips
and your teeth. I like your mother for making you wear braces. I
also like your mother because she gave you your: size, shape, coloring, unselfishness, good table manners, fashion sense, truthfulness,
and because she spared you her own corny sense of humor."

I picked her up and felt my chronic bad back throw itself out.
The pain would be unbearable in a few minutes; it always took five
to ten minutes for the aggravated xylophone bone at the base of my
spine to send the note of pain trembling up and down the keyboard.

Before my torso surrendered to the inevitable ess the pain would
shape itself into, I carried my wife to the bedroom and lay her on the
unspread covers. When we were newlyweds, I used to use Henny
Youngman's joke to tease her about her neatness. "Last night," I'd
say, "I woke up to go to the bathroom, and when I came back the
bed was made." But for the past few years, it wasn't all that unusual
for me to find our bed at night exactly as I had left it that morning.

When I tried to pull the bunched covers out from beneath my

wife, the sting in my back stopped every bit of strength. The more I exerted my arms or legs, the more painful the forming ess became. The only good feature of my back trouble was that I could always find one position in which the pain was bearable; this time I found it at the foot of the bed, curled at my wife's feet, my own feet tucked up like a foetus's, my head on its side, my eyes staring along the unflattering wifescape. I noticed that she was not breathing. I noticed that her flattened breasts did not prevent cubist folds from inhabiting her blowsy plaid shirt. It was as if death had shrunk her, run over her like a steamroller. She had found the one position in which her pain was bearable.

We lay like that awhile, neither of us able to speak.

If now I wanted to write a new list of things about her that I liked, that I would like despite being in love with her, what might they be?

I like the way you've let yourself go. I like the same faded jeans you wear every day. I like the gallows humor you find in all our most serious problems. I like the way you call the kids "imbecile," "jerk," "moron." I like the inane TV shows you're addicted to. I like the fact that you're always on the verge of crying.

It was more painful than my back to go on inventorying the bad stock of our last few years. Even more depressing was the realization that I had not been terribly unhappy—except about the older boy, whose sad future preyed on me whenever I allowed my mind a moment's idleness, which I worked hard to avoid.

The other night on the Johnny Carson show a country-and-western singer who had a hit I'd been hearing twice a day—to and from the train station—mouthed the plaintive words of her twangy dirge imprisoned by bolts of garish spotlights. There was no way to recreate the echoey magic of the hit song—a song my company had tested and correctly predicted would be a hit—except by playing the original while the sparrowy widow of the lyrics pretended she was singing. But her lips were always a beat behind the words. When the real singer pretended to hope "he's only sleeping," the once-real singer was already beginning to moan "but now it's always the middle of the night for me."

I, too, was always a beat behind. While I had been pretending the last few years were happy, the once-real me—the original, complicated me I could not re-create—was already beginning to mourn. When my wife and I agreed to become engaged, we had already been acting married. She had realized that life with me was as good as her life could be. I had made up my mind not to court disaster. I knew my wife. I knew her moods. I knew how to make her happy. Why risk a sure sense of manhood by discovering that other women had to be worked differently and that if I tangled up their strings I might never get their legs to spread.

Her mother had disapproved of the engagement, and that had been the source of coldness between mother and daughter until our first son was born. Until he was conceived, actually.

"You've got a lifetime. Why don't you wait a while?" her mother had counseled, but both of us heard what she was really saying: "Don't wind up like me, make something of yourself, don't get married to the first one who comes along, go to graduate school, be a biologist, he's twenty years old—my God, what does he know at twenty that he won't know better at twenty-five?"

Two hours earlier we had watched Popeye and Bluto pulverize each other at a campus film festival. The baby Sweet Pea had been crawling about on the slippery deck of Popeye's ship while the two tars warred over the love of a shrieking Olive Oyl, who had lashed herself to the mast by her own ropy arms in a fit of hysteria. Because even a cartoon became the subject of intellectual analysis at a campus film festival, I had said to my wife that the Popeye characters were symbolic.

"What?" she laughed.

"It's true. Think about it. Popeye is a good man who has to eat his spinach—in other words he has to know and accept what's good for him—in order to triumph over Bluto, who is a bad man. Meanwhile Olive Oyl is always running around screaming like a banshee because she doesn't know how things are going to turn out. Maybe that big ugly brute will beat up Popeye and stick his hairy baseball bat right up Olive's screamin' little Mimi. It's like you and me and Bruce Mathias."

"I certainly didn't scream."

"No . . ."

"And you certainly didn't eat your spinach and make a muscle and come looking for Bruce."

"I didn't have to. Good always triumphs over evil."

"So you think I'm Olive Oyl," she had shrieked, pulling out her ears and popping her eyes to look the part. I laughed out loud. So much of her humor was cerebral that an occasional physical joke always caught me by surprise. It was always a treat to see her subvert her good looks for a good laugh. Her one open eye seemed to bulge a little now or was it the angle?

"Actually," I remembered, "you're not a bit like Olive Oyl. She's much too serious about life. You're more like Sweet Pea, just merrily crawling along the floor while the whole world is going crazy all around you."

"Neenoo, neenoo, goo goo."

"Hey, Sweet Pea . . ."

"Nanoo, nanoo?"

"Marry me?"

"Neeno, nanoo, neenoo!"

Margaret Kovac had been more than my wife's matron of honor. She had been a sort of matron saint of marriage, a real life example of how the right guy could keep you from losing your mind. Margaret Kovac had swallowed up Margaret Hennesy and shit her out. The Kovacs' wedding present was now hanging in the dining room: a cheerful Corot landscape, distinguished mainly by three blurry lasses who appear to be gathering moss.

The only serious conversation I was ever to have with my mother-in-law had lasted half a dance at the wedding. "I know you know I was not happy about this," she waltzed me around, "but I'm happy now. I only want you two to be happy. Me, I made my bed. But you two have the rest of your lives together. Please, make her happy. I know you will. But maybe she doesn't know what's good for her. She should go to graduate school and be somebody. Married life is wonderful, but . . ." and then her husband cut in before she could tell me what really must have been on her mind.

"Will you marry me, Sweet Pea?" I asked my dead wife. "Will you swear to be my wife for better or worse? This time I'll make you go to graduate school. This time we'll save our money instead of going on a honeymoon. We'll work hard, both of us, biology and market research, and we won't have kids—we'll never have kids— we'll travel and buy a boat and have a country house with a den and a greenhouse and a town house in the city with a terra cotta terrace and maid service and a chauffeur to take us to dinner and Broadway and dancing at the Rainbow Room. This time I'll pay attention to you. I won't leave you alone. No one will break in and rape you while I'm on a business trip. No one will put her exotic hand against my crotch and whisper, 'Let Deborah teach you a thing or two about Cleveland, Ohio—no strings attached.'"

The honeymoon was the last time my wife was unconditionally happy. There was absolutely nothing else to worry about. She had not yet turned down her fellowship for graduate school. We had not yet accustomed ourselves to a strict budget. Her mother's lifelong heart problem had not yet begun to deteriorate. Kids were years away. Life was purely a run in the sand, multicolored cocktails, fluorescent skies, nightclubs, sidewalk cafes, zoos, historical landmarks, botanical gardens and boats-bikes-cars-horses-to-hire whose only mission was to make us want to come back again for another dip or sip or glimpse or gallop through paradise.

There might be shells in the bags. She gathered them the last day of our honeymoon as though she could take pieces of paradise home with her. Or her bridal bouquet. Or my list of likes. Or her poetry.

At that moment I would have leaped to my wife's dresser drawer, pulled out the two bags, and ripped them open. But just glancing toward the dresser shot a vibrato of pain through my back, as if the tiny muscles of my eyes were directly connected to the massive muscles which formed the hard cruel ess.

I found my position again. It had shifted slightly. I had to untuck my legs a bit. Despite a twinge of pain, I rested one arm on my wife's leg, willing it there until I did not mind the little twinge and could touch my wife lovingly without having to concentrate on doing so. In a while the pain in my back would soften. It would be difficult, but I would be able to sit up, stand up, walk to the dresser, open the drawer, take out the bags, and discover once and for all what she had saved. Chances were I had already missed my guess. From the moment we got off the plane at the end of our honeymoon, her life was not worth saving.

"Tell me the truth, dog honest, do you really want to go to graduate school?" I had asked during the first of the more than four thousand dinners she was to cook for us. (The night I brought home a pocket calculator we figured out how many meals she had made, how many cigarettes I'd smoke if I lived to be eighty, how many doodies she'd cleaned, spills she'd mopped, orgasms we'd have, seconds we'd lived.)

"Because if you do want to go, then you should. We can manage. I'll be earning more money in a year. Maybe twice as much. But if you don't want to, then you shouldn't just go through the motions."

I knew she wanted to give up the fellowship. Textbooks made her feel like a child. Cooking and cleaning and going to work and putting her own income into her own savings account would make her feel like a woman. She needed me to say it was all right. She needed her husband to help her contradict her mother. A wife was more powerful than a daughter. A wife could do things a daughter could not.

"I don't think your mother ever forgave me. I don't think you ever forgave me. either," I said to my dead wife. I squeezed her leg and was surprised that it felt as it had a thousand times before. The words of the hit song struck me: she's only sleeping. I thought of my mother trying to wake up my father's corpse. I remembered countless poems in which death was symbolized by sleep, without remembering any specific line of any specific poem. I wondered why the third of a lifetime we spent sleeping didn't prepare us any better.

"Wake up."

I squeezed her thigh gently. I shook her slightly.

"Sweet Pea, it's late."

She hardly slept at all in the beginning. She was awake when I went to sleep at night, and she was awake when I got up in the morning. She threw herself into our first year of marriage like a hopeful actress auditioning for the part. She tried everything: gourmet dinners, the latest decorating ideas, outrageous clothes and makeup, wild haircuts, a different perfume every night, sexual diagrams drawn from the pages of any and every obscure love guide, and, of course, the constant nervous chattering of her wit. I must admit that I liked it, although I was never quite sure who she was trying to convince, me or her. But a man would be a fool not to enjoy it while it lasted.

The night before I left for Buffalo on my first business trip, the night before her sophomore came to call, every mad excess of the entire year seemed to come together and come between us.

For dinner she was preparing mutton, and the smell reminded me of a locker room. I told her I probably hated mutton, whereupon, with no hard feelings, she tossed the half-cooked sheep's flesh into the garbage and said, "Let's go out, then." Fifteen minutes later she emerged from the bathroom—which she used as a dressing room when she wanted to surprise me—wearing a blood red mini-dress that barely covered the leg bands of her blue panties. All I could stammer was a silly warning about catching a cold. Her hair was longish that week and braided. Her eyes were purple blobs of silver-specked paint. But she did not look ridiculous. She looked like the secretaries who worked in my office. But that was in New York, in Manhattan, and my wife was about to parade her Fauvist smudge of an outfit a million miles away in New Jersey.

I pictured a battered actress's battered makeup kit and yellowed scripts (her own lines underscored in faded red) and dusty props stolen as *memento mori* and a batch of floridly written reviews whose old-fashioned precepts dated them even more than the crumbling news stock. Spiders locked them up. The granular sunbeam that breaks through an attic window illuminated the contents of my wife's secret bags. Surely I had missed my guess. Most likely they contained the wind that had been knocked out of her.

At dinner, she made me order for her.

"What are you in the mood for?" I asked.

"Mutton," she said, as though the idea had just hit her. It was an Italian restaurant.

Most of the dinner conversation was centered around my trip. She was jealous without saying so. A business trip was a much more powerful symbol of adulthood than a mini-dress. "It's like a *bar mitzvah*," she had said. "Tomorrow, when you get on the plane and order a martini and flirt with a stewie, you will be a man."

"What will you do while I'm away?" I asked her.

"I was thinking of taking this opportuntiy to repaint the apartment."

I looked around the bedroom. Every wall of our house was off-white, yellow actually, from four packs of cigarettes a day. My wife's three and my one in the evening, after work.

During coffee my wife had opened her handbag and taken out a pack of cigarettes.

"What the hell is that?"

"I've decided to smoke."

"You're crazy."

"*You* smoke."

"I'm crazy."

She lit up and choked on the first few puffs.

"Real satisfying, huh?" I said sarcastically.

"You should have heard me this morning," she laughed.

"Why are you doing this? Jesus, if I wasn't hooked—"

"Look around the room," she said. "Everyone is smoking."

"That's because they started when they were kids, like me. Do you think I'd start now? It's insane. It kills you."

I'd picked up the habit during the summer we didn't see each other. Not smoking while you were heaving cinder blocks or pouring cement or fitting Sheetrock was like walking onto the construction site with a violin case. My wife had laughed her nervous laugh when she saw my new habit at the camp weekend. She'd even called me crazy. But cigarettes were a blessing that weekend. For hours on end I watched my own smoke fill the bunkhouse as if it were the exhaust from my racing anger. That was when the habit clicked.

"I'm not going to do it all day long. Just at certain special times. After dinner. After sex." She winked at me. "I'm never going to smoke as much as you do. That really is crazy."

I couldn't argue with her. My annoyance made me light up three cigarettes in quick succession, one of them before I had half finished the one I was already smoking. Instead, I told her an appropriate story that my boss had told me that very day. I told her that originally Marlboros had been designed as a woman's cigarette. "The first Marlboros had red filter tips," I had said, "so that a woman's lipstick wouldn't show. But it wasn't until they switched to a regular filter and came up with the Marlboro Man campaign that women started buying them."

"The only reason I bought Marlboros," she explained, a bit too defensively, "is because you smoke them. Now there'll always be a pack in the house in case you run out of yours when the stores are closed."

Later, when we were home, she looked at me with sex expression number five from some Hindu sex text and said, "You know something?"

"What?"

She drew her legs up so her blue panties were completely exposed.

"I think I'm going to really want a cigarette about an hour from now."

That was the last time we ever made love alone. Without the leering presence of the sophomore.

She looked now as she must have when that maniac made her get into bed and then sniffed her up and down. She must have been too scared to move. She must have been scared to death. When I realized that my hand had traveled from my dead wife's thigh to between her legs, I pulled my hand away and looked at it. It was numb.

"Shake it," she had said, lighting up one of my Marlboros. "When my arm falls asleep, I shake it. Sometimes you have to bang it against something to get the circulation going."

We had worked hard to get into the prescribed position. When finally we were in place, the weight of both our bodies had humped deliriously against my pinned arm. The next morning I flew to Buffalo. It was the farthest away from my wife that I had ever been in all the years we had known each other. It was where I had my first look through a one-way mirror. It was where my specific ambition within the general discipline of market research began.

A pocket of pain formed above my right eye and pulsed as far as the temple. The whole right side of my head felt congested, gummy inside, except for the oasis of pain.

If I had to identify the precise beginning, the particular events which started us on our separate ways, I would be forced to point to my wife's confrontation with the sophomore and my own spying on Larraine, whose name and overdone face still remained only a pane of one-way glass away from deepest memory. But of course, the beginnings were not that specific. Couldn't I just as easily point to my wife's decision not to go to graduate school, to go to work instead? To work for me. And my secret enjoyment, the power I felt as she tried to impress and amuse and flatter and hold onto her boss.

I craved her. She was mine. When I talked about her to the people I worked with, it was another way of talking about myself. Modestly I could boast about the incredibly bright, funny, pretty woman who was waiting for me at home, who would use her remarkable organizational ability to sort my socks, who would shine her stunning creativity on my dinner plate, who would flutter the wings of her wit just to make me laugh, who would choreograph starkly lit moves in bed to make me forget the smallness of her breasts, who would exercise her idle twenty-one credits of botany by breeding frisky, wet-nosed plant life in every cranny of our one-room apartment—for me to admire. And for her to breathe. Everything else took her breath away. But her plants—the nervous ivy, the humping piggybacks, the creeping spiders and bulging jades and lazy cacti—they kept her alive.

Without tilting my aching head or moving the back-connected muscles of my eyes, I saw the arrangement of dried flowers on my wife's dresser. Cattails. Eucalyptus. Baby's breath. No living plant had been in the house since we moved in. The older boy had a tendency to eat things. The younger boy had a tendency to run over things. My wife had a tendency to drop watering to the bottom of her longer and longer list of chores.

Yes, the episode with the sophomore had been awful, harrowing, traumatic. For both of us. And Larraine's face behind the one-way mirror in Buffalo had been inspirational, shocking almost—to think that I could reach that deeply into reality without having to give up a thing of myself.

But really those events were only convenient symbols of everything else that was going on in our lives.

Just as awful was the role of a married woman which my Sweet Pea tried squeezing into as though it were a red mini-dress that barely covered her baby bottom. But, in fact, as snug as that dress was, it had been a thousand sizes too big. The role had been too big. She tried to fill it with mutton and eye shadow and sex books and cigarette smoke and two ballooning bellies full of new life, but it was impossible to fill. And the fun she had trying soon turned to frustrating hard work. To despair.

It is too big an idea, the idea of being a woman. Too grand. My wife did not lose heart because she wished she had become someone or something important—a biologist, a comedienne, a poet. She lost faith. Because the role of woman is unfulfillable.

My manhood had flourished.

"I want you to hire a secretary for yourself," my boss had told me on the plane to Buffalo, a double Beefeater sloshing in his plastic cup, occasionally spilling over onto his vested suit. "But I want you to hire someone with big tits. You can teach typing, you can't teach tits."

I had laughed a knowing laugh, having had to invent one on the spur of the moment. It is unbearable for me to think now that I might have been laughing then at my own wife's small breasts.

Larraine's face had made mine light up. I could see her putting on her makeup, but she could not see me. The sophomore could see my wife, but my wife would not see him. Our roles were defined forever.

If she had told me about the sophomore, instead of telling my mother and swearing her to secrecy, perhaps all this would not have happened. If she had made me face what she had faced, I might have comforted her, seen her side of things. But when I looked at her, I saw a terribly confused and frightened specimen, not a woman who was willing to fight, but a woman who sensed her own incapacities and, by accepting them, convinced me that it was the law of the jungle.

And yet, was I so wrong? Had I been a typical domineering, insensitive, purely lustful husband? I had not. I'd simply been incapable of talking to her. Unwilling to reach in and really touch her where it counted. And that, too, was the law of the jungle.

Afraid. That was the word that kept coming up over and over again. Afraid to talk. Afraid to reveal. Afraid to share. Afraid that if the costumed, scripted roles of husband and wife fluffed a line or dropped a prop, the curtain would ring down on the only lives either of us could envision for ourselves.

"Damn."

The secretary I had hired had had the biggest tits of all who applied for the job. They were grotesque. The flesh billowed up over the straining necklines of the low-cut peasant dresses she wore. But beneath her shimmering flesh beat an understanding and anxious heart.

I spent many casual hours interviewing her on the subject of rape, food, marriage, bad habits, and whatever else I needed to discuss with someone, anyone, anyone but my wife. I told myself that I was practicing for an eventual career as a focus group moderator.

In that role I could keep a comfortable distance. Whatever information I gleaned was data, not innermost feeling. I found that I had a knack for phrasing my inquiries in such a way as to make my otherwise circumspect secretary talk endlessly about her own life, the details of which were not nearly as interesting as her quick desire to speak them.

I have forgotten her name. I have forgotten also the expression in her eyes. I remember only the chattering of joke-store teeth and her huge breasts and an inch or two of the usual paisley that hemmed her jiggling flesh and an occasional lewd wink from a coworker because I had seen nothing wrong, nothing even remotely adulterous about taking my secretary to lunch or for an after-hours drink so that I could continue my apprenticeship.

Or had I been speaking to my wife through my secretary, as my wife might have been speaking to me through the future Mrs. Alan Kovac?

"It hurt you, didn't it? My career," I said into the muffle of covers. I was lost now in remembrances. The bed, my wife, the dried flowers, the secret bags, everything vanished, and my memory soared through time and space with nothing to anchor it but the covers smothering the senses of smell, sight, taste, and touch and the vague pains, which felt like a single pain, running from head to toe.

•

We never really tried to get back on the right track. Or onto the same track. We moved to a new apartment, and my wife thanked me by making love for the first time since the sophomore made his perverse one-way love to her in my absence. But rather than a flash of things to come, her genuine passion was actually a glimmer of things that had passed. Determined to know once and for all if it was she, if she was uniquely winded, my wife scoured our new neighborhood for women her own age and in her own circumstances. But the women she had found were either mothers or pregnant or trying to become pregnant. The one she liked best was Madelaine, who suspected that her husband was physically incapable of impregnating her. "He can make love, but not babies," Madelaine told my wife. "But he won't see a doctor. I've been. The doctor told me that I'm healthy. But Mickey won't go. And he won't adopt. He says it's just nerves or something. I think he's just afraid to face it."

My wife did not ask Madelaine the inevitable logical question that she did ask me: what good will it do anyway for Mickey to find out that he's sterile? They still won't be able to have a kid.

In my boundless remembrances time did not matter; my memory jumped to a day that did not actually happen, a day in which two events incredibly coincided, though in reality the two events happened weeks, maybe months apart.

I had arrived at my office and found a sealed envelope on my desk. It was addressed to me in my secretary's tiny handwriting, a hand that could fit the New Testament on one of her pancake-sized (I imagined) nipples. Inside the envelope I found more of her impossibly microscopic penmanship, two pages worth, fronts and backs.

It was a blubbery letter of resignation. The sentiments shook like her breasts. People were beginning to talk, she had written; she herself was beginning to worry that what was being whispered behind our backs would hurt someone; she had one rule she would not break because of something about the shoe being on the other foot; I will not steal another woman's husband; it is not you who is to blame, you have been a perfect gentleman; I'm sick about my love for you; I can barely stand being in the same building with you; and then four indiscreet paragraphs concerning the sexual fantasies my apprenticeship had apparently aroused, during which her handwriting grew to twice its normal size; and in conclusion I'm never setting foot in your place again for the good of all concerned; I'll miss you.

That night Madelaine answered the door when I arrived home. She had been crying earlier and was evidently trying to busy herself to keep from crying again.

My wife had called me aside while Madelaine closed the door behind me and returned to the kitchen where she had been washing a few of our dishes. Shushing me and pulling me out of Madelaine's earshot my wife led me to the bedroom, sat me on the bed, and in her most serious woman's voice told me the fantastic details. The story was so unbelievable I overlooked the mismatch of her young, high-pitched, punch-line-prone voice and the excruciatingly adult tone it was trying in vain to strike. Madelaine had told Mickey that their prayers had been answered. She'd been to the doctor and he had confirmed it; they were pregnant. They?

"But I thought . . ."

Again she shushed me. By shaking her head knowingly.

"Is she really pregnant?"

My wife continued to shake her head yes.

When she told him, he went crazy. He began yelling and crying, and then he grabbed his razor, punched her good-bye and left forever.

"He punched her? She looked all right just now."

"He punched her in the stomach."

Madelaine stayed the night, intermittently crying and pretending that our apartment was hers, that I was Mickey, that my wife was her child.

"I thought you hated peas," she said to me at dinner.

"You've been in the bathtub for an hour," she cautioned my wife, "you'll turn into a prune."

I slept on the couch so the two of them could say what they had to on into the night. Before turning out the light, I reread my secretary's letter. Before I fell asleep, I imagined Mickey and my secretary meeting each other. The scene was the bar where on occasion I had treated her to more than I had realized. Mickey was attracted to her huge breasts. My secretary was attracted to Mickey's huge melancholy, which bespoke a new aloneness. This time she would not have to consider breaking her rule; Mickey's grim face, trying its best to smile, told her that the rule had already been broken. They would be good for each other, I daydreamed. My secretary looked like a woman who could get pregnant just by talking about it.

The next day Madelaine had gone back home to her own apartment, hoping to find her husband. But she never saw him again. That evening, after work, I stopped at my local bar for a drink, hoping to find my secretary waiting at our customary table in the front room, right by the window, where anyone who knew either of us could see that we were having a business meeting. But I never saw my secretary again.

Mickey Junior had survived the punch and was put up for adoption. His real father adopted him a year later. His real father's wife loved him as if he were her own flesh and blood. Madelaine moved to California and wrote my wife one letter. The first page incoherently praised the glories of heroin. The second page begged for money. In Cleveland, on a business trip, I thought I saw my former secretary hailing a taxi, but when she turned my way to back into the cab she was twenty years too old. A week after walking out on Madelaine, Mickey called my wife in the middle of the afternoon, quite drunk, and asked if she'd like to suck his enormous cock. She thought she had let Madelaine down by not keeping him on the phone long enough to have the call traced.

•

My career had flourished. It was not a case of being married to my work—I never earned truly seductive amounts of money or fame or responsibility or power. I was simply fascinated by my business, loving it in the same way one can't put down a good book or walk out on a good movie, and I had always marveled at my good fortune to have been able to earn a better and better living doing what I so thoroughly enjoyed. Not everyone was as lucky in that respect. Most of the men of my generation despised their jobs. A butcher my age had committed suicide by closing himself inside his meat locker. When I read about it in the newspaper, I had thought that it might just as easily have been a chiropractor mashed beneath his hydraulic table, or a stockbroker strangled by bearish ticker tape, or a regional sales manager who drove off the edge of his territory, or a soap opera actor who wrote himself out of life's script, or an assistant buyer smothered by unsellable merchandise, or a garage mechanic found hovering over his air pump, his mouth clamped around the nozzle of the hose, his cartoon body straining toward eternity like a float in Macy's Thanksgiving Day Parade.

I knew these men. I grew up with them. Others I interviewed. Despite their bitterness, most refused to die. Their suicide was a tiredness, as if they were consciously committing themselves to sleep. Their jobs weighed on them, separated their skin from their bones, slowed their walks—except on the golf course.

But my wife had not refused to die. Or to be murdered by circumstances.

My work was all about conclusions. Clients came to me because they did not know how America felt, and I would ask America and then tell my clients how America felt. Sometimes America was two hundred people, sometimes only twelve. It depended on how unsure the clients were and how much of an investment was riding on the conclusions I might draw.

Ninety-nine times out of a hundred, my conclusions would be negative. The business was constructed in such a way as to constantly, consistently validate itself. If America always wanted what my clients suspected it wanted, there would be little need for people like me. I knew that. So my research—all research—consisted of elaborate systems of negative analysis, systems veiled in a psycho-physio-analytic mystique. My job was to measure America's innermost feelings by galvanometer, by group dynamic, by Freudian probe, by hook or by crook, to extract these feelings and then measure them against how America should feel. And if my company wanted to earn its money, I had better find some serious negative feelings. That justified what the client was charged. That made the client trust us. And himself.

What if I put my wife under the test? What if I analyzed her life for that period of several years during which my ambition had metamorphosed into a career? What conclusions could I force?

There were several ways to do it. She could reenact her life on a stage while America watched and kept one hand on a dial that recorded enthusiasm and approval, or boredom and disapproval, each step of the way.

My wife begins to wake up in the morning a little later than she used to; it's not that she means to, but her sleep is so deep she doesn't always respond to the alarm. She hears it, turns it off, but thinks it's a dream and goes back to sleep. DISAPPROVAL. America thinks of itself as an early morning country. The early bird gets the worm, up and at 'em, etc.

She does not spend a full hour dressing and putting on her makeup. Her good wardrobe and expensive tubes, jars, cakes, bottles, and sprays of prettiness make it impossible for her to leave for work any less than well-groomed and fashionable, but her heart does not seem to be in it. Perhaps when the various containers are empty and her clothes too worn, she will not replace them in kind. DISAPPROVAL. Clothes make the man. The closer he gets, the better she looks, etc. America calls itself The Beautiful.

For breakfast she drinks three cups of coffee and smokes a cigarette with each cup. The routine is so familiar that if she says she drinks three cigarettes and smokes three cups of coffee she would not notice the spoonerism. DISAPPROVAL. The most important meal of the day is breakfast. Kellogg's says the best to you each morning. America fuels up on bacon, eggs, flapjacks, muffins, oatmeal, o.j., donuts, etc.

Her workday must be tested differently, if it can be tested at all. I only suspect that it, too, lost its snap, crackle, and pop after her episode with the sophomore and my episode with Larraine. She never talked about it. She seemed increasingly tired at the end of each day, as though her secretarial job at the biology department were draining her. But precise, measurable details were not known. It may not matter. Not everything is knowable. It was hardly unusual for a research document to point out one or more unknown factors. It even worked to the researcher's advantage, exonerating his potentially erroneous conclusions. More than once I have had to explain my disproved findings by admitting that I had simply guessed wrong regarding the unknowable.

My wife comes home and unwraps her second pack of cigarettes. In the beginning she cooks only classic dishes. But it seems more to the point, more typical of the direction she's moving in, that she happens to pick a recipe for Hamburger Stroganoff which she finds on the label of a can of Campbell's Cream of Chicken Soup. Of course the undiluted contents of the can are a main ingredient. The recipe can vary only insofar as the grade of meat and the amounts of spices used. Every time my wife cooks Campbell's Hamburger Stroganoff it tastes different. She puts in more salt than the recipe calls for. Or she switches to a leaner or fattier choice of beef. Or she sprinkles too much or too little parsley. DISAPPROVAL. America believes in giving and following precise instructions.

So automatic is the switching on of the TV as we sit down to dinner that it might in fact be the switching off of the oven. My wife not only watches TV all night, but she refers to the various programs as hers. "My doctor show is on in a minute." "My lawyer show is going to be good tonight." It is amazing that she continues to be witty. I have always equated wit with intelligence and television with dumbness. DISAPPROVAL. Television *is* a vast wasteland. America prefers a Norman Rockwell dinner, the remotest cousin present, a holiday turkey about to be carved by Dad, and then a full-bellied evening out on the porch or beside the roaring fire, the glazed conversation touching on everything from that good marmalade dressing to Sunday's sermon.

Conversation. Two or three times during commercial or network breaks my wife is about to say something. You can tell by her expression that it is important. But she always thinks again about saying what's on her mind, and by that time her program is back on the air. *No reading*—neither approval nor disapproval. America does not realize that this is conversation. America thinks it is a continuation of watching TV on which it has already dialed its DISAPPROVAL.

The phone rings. It is my wife's mother. My wife only answers questions, does not ask any other than an obviously insincere "How are you and Dad?" DISAPPROVAL. America loves its mother, would kill for the Motherland. In the melting pot, generational differences of opinion boil away. Oedipus and Lear could not happen here.

She wears a nightgown. She did not even bring one along on our honeymoon. There are knots now that must be untied before we can make love. She leaves the position up to me. Her moaning is internal. I must guess whether or not a particular strategy of love is working. More often than not I judge by her complacency. Complacency seems to be the theme of her life. If she cries out or winces and moves my fingers away from her nipple, then I know to change my strategy. If she sobs or screams or complains of cramps or of a toothache or has a coughing fit or stays home from work, then I know something is wrong. Otherwise, I assume she is happy. It is her life. It is the bed she has made. I can only assume that she is as happy with her life as I am with mine. And I do not disdain her brand of happiness. I deal in the way things are. DISAPPROVAL. America is uneasy about sex. It prefers an unlit stage. America likes to do it in the dark.

At the climax of our lovemaking, I more than make up for her demure hip-wriggles and clenched teeth. I scream out, I try to make my body move in circles, I turn up the volume of my panting until the tone is deafening. My orgasm is a grand mal seizure of shivers and flailing and grunts and squeals that builds and builds to an immense stop. And then I collapse into post-ecstasy. A few seconds later my wife says, "Did you come?" APPROVAL. America has a great sense of humor.

In terms of Immediate Interest, with one exception, America disapproves of everything my wife does. As it watches her, it doesn't like her. But the crucial test comes later. America has seen many women in similar circumstances. Will America remember my wife, think more kindly of her after some time to reflect?

I watch America sit down in front of my one-way mirror. The moderator tries to set a comfortable tone. He compliments a dress, envies a beard, pinches the cheek of a little girl.

America does remember. My wife was a slight woman who did not seem terribly ambitious. She seemed resigned, sedated by a life of TV. She did say something funny, but America doesn't remember exactly what it was. Something about the joke struck America as odd. My wife's sense of humor was definitely intrusive, it seemed inappropriate and confusing. America doesn't think a dull life is funny. America thrives on adventure.

I sat behind memory's one-way mirror and tried to defend my findings. But I could not exonerate myself. There was no unknowable factor. I did know that my wife was hurt by my commitment to my career, even if indirectly. I had fit into my adulthood so much more snugly than she had been able to fit into hers. Everyone knew it. Everyone thought so. Our dinner guests patronized my wife. They made a huge fuss over small matters. They seemed to have to search for conversation. Desperately they welcomed the quip they knew she'd sooner or later make as her only real contribution to the dinner party, to the evening, to the world.

Her wit became the very essence of her. She joked about everything. She took nothing seriously. I'd find myself pre-examining whatever I was about to say for potential straight lines. I'd find myself disparaging other people's accomplishments merely because their fine deeds had not been done with a sense of humor. I purposely mistook my wife's jokes as a sign that she was happy. But she was not happy. My mistake had been in thinking that her unhappiness was an immutable fact of life. I did not see my own contribution to it nor realize that I might have helped. I was too happy being left alone. My wife did not ask for help, and I did not offer any. She only joked. I only laughed.

Jill Farkus Johanson's infant son Paul suffocated one night in his crib. At the funeral my wife asked me in a whisper if the somber men carrying the grotesquely small casket were Paul bearers.

While crossing the street together, a huge truck nearly ran us over, to which my wife remarked: God! We were almost struck down in the prime of our ribs.

She informed me over the phone of an automobile accident she and the garage had had by asking if I remembered where it said FIREBIRD on the side of the car. When I told her that I did remember, she reported that now it said FBRIEDIR.

She was very funny. Was it any wonder that I half expected her to sit straight up in bed now and elbow me in the ribs?

But there was a lack of compassion in her humor. Mostly she was cynical and morbid and spiteful. It was humor that did not last, could not be retold. It failed to ennoble its pitiful subjects.

She took her father's pulse one evening as a way of telling him that he was not exactly the life of the party. She wondered out loud whether Margaret Kovac would ever tell her snub-nosed, sallow-faced Korean child that he was adopted. She told my boss that he was not as fat and ugly as I had been saying. It took a full ten seconds for the tall, slim, extremely handsome head of my company to laugh. I had counted.

I should have listened more closely to her jokes. Perhaps the bitterness of her life expressed itself in the punch lines. Perhaps if I had rearranged the words like the letters of FIREBIRD, I would have heard her asking me for help, telling me that she had been in some sort of accident with life. Maybe it was only a scrape. Maybe it could have been pounded out of her like the dent in a fender. But I was too busy laughing. Too busy pretending everything was fine.

At work, everything was better than fine. I had a natural talent for interviewing. The following I had begun to pick up translated to a quick succession of healthy raises. Left to my own devices, I fine-tuned my focus group interview technique and then began to train others as moderators. It was during the period of transition from in front of the mirror to behind it that my life turned suddenly serious.

I met Deborah. Not Debbie. Not Deb. Deborah.

Deborah was a screener. Her job was to enlist focus groups and screen out those people whose age or income or occupation or marital status or race or religion or sexual preferences or physical features or political affiliations were not desirable. Of course, sometimes her job had to be performed quite delicately. The groups I had requested of Deborah, for example, were to be comprised of young men, boys really, on the verge or just past the verge of shaving for the first time. It had been a hurried request; I had called Deborah's Cleveland office only two days before I wanted the groups to be scheduled. She had to get her young men any way she could, but quickly. She contacted the principals of several local high schools and asked them for a list of the freshman class, explaining why and assuring the skeptical principals that there was nothing improper or devious about her request. Finally one principal agreed. Then Deborah had to make phone calls, one hundred or more. It hadn't been as simple as asking Master Albert or Master Peter or Master Richard if he were planning or had just executed his first shave. Blacks were unwanted. And so was a certain scruffy element. And anyone with severe, unshavable acne. Delicately, Deborah had to screen the undesirables over the phone. Three or four misfits made it through a tear in her screen, but the groups, by and large, were outstanding. My client, a small metal goods company in Cincinnati which had previously specialized in kitchen gadgets, was sufficiently encouraged by the results of my focus group to manufacture and promote "Baby Face," a triply-safe razor blade designed for uninitiated cheeks and necks. Although seventy percent of the boys in Deborah's interview room had said they would buy "Baby Face" at least once, when the blades appeared in Cincinnati drugstores and supermarkets, so did a new Gillette razor, the head of which could be adjusted to expose varying degrees of a blade, any blade, a Gillette blade, a better and less expensive blade than "Baby Face." Acme Metal Goods discontinued "Baby Face." But I did not discontinue my relationship with Deborah Satin. Immediately I had thought of her as a midwest affiliate. If ever I needed groups in her territory, Deborah would be the one to enlist them.

I saw her now as she appeared to me when I first saw her: a tall, ample woman surrounded by dozens of teenage boys. She was wearing a pantsuit, gray, and a white silk blouse setting off and set off by a maroon necktie that seemed to pour from a perfect Windsor knot. Her hair was short, mannish, but softer and freer than a man would have it. The sharp features of her face looked natural, though a close look revealed every kind of facial makeup— lipstick, eye shadow, eyeliner, base, rouge—each applied with wisdom and finesse. Naturally I jumped to the unfair conclusion that Deborah Satin's efficiency, businesslike attitude, and masculine demeanor compromised, if not completely repressed, her hetero-sexuality. I soon found out how far that was from the truth. Once again I had guessed wrong regarding the unknowable.

"It's too late to find a decent restaurant in Cleveland," she had said, after the last group of boys had filed out and we could turn on the light in the viewing room. "Even your hotel kitchen will be closed at this hour. And you look like the kind of man who'd love a steak right now. I happen to have one in my freezer."

In my heart I told my wife that it was okay; Deborah Satin was just a good businesswoman trying to get in the good graces of someone who was in the position of giving her work from time to time. Besides, with the exception of her name, there was not a seductive thing about her.

She lived in a house. That surprised me. I could not afford such a luxury at that time, although prices in suburban Cleveland were not what they were in New Jersey or Long Island or anywhere else within commuting distance of Manhattan. The house was small but strangely spacious. It might have been my own uneasiness about being in the unchaperoned company of an unfamiliar woman late at night, but when I walked across the living room, which I did several times while Deborah seasoned and cooked our steak dinners, I felt like a small boy, and the wall to wall trip took an eternity. I felt as if I were in the palatial room of a museum; I knew I should not touch the exhibits, but I felt a mischievous urge to put a quick finger on the imposing grand piano, on the black leather wing-back chair, on the crushed-velvet sofa, on the marble coffee table. I satisfied my desire by taking a candy from the crystal bowl on top of the marble table. Nothing else invited touching. Including Deborah.

We sat at opposite ends of a long mahogany table during dinner.

We talked about our businesses through the main course. We talked about Cleveland over coffee. She refused a cigarette, explaining unsentimentally that both her mother and father had died of lung cancer.

"What do you think of Cleveland?" she asked.

"It closes pretty early," I joked.

"Most New Yorkers hate it."

"I haven't seen enough to hate."

"They think it's got all the disadvantages of a big city and a small town. Slums, ugly skyscrapers, traffic, noise, crime, a filthy river on the one hand. A smug, provincial lack of adventure and idealism on the other."

"Sounds to me like you believe it."

"No," she said, rising from her end of our table like a schoolteacher rising from behind her desk to dramatize a correction that had to be made because a small boy had guessed wrong and she did not want him ever to make the same mistake again.

"I love Cleveland," she instructed me, "because it's anonymous. Because there's a freedom in Cleveland that you can't find in New York or in Sioux City."

She walked to me, and her eyes commanded me to stand up, which I did. It was uncomfortable to be dwarfed by a woman.

"Nothing matters, you see, in Cleveland. Anything goes. It's too big to be gossipy and too small to be interesting even to its own inhabitants. No one is very possessive about Cleveland. Except me. To be perfectly candid, I'm a wealthy woman. My parents left huge insurance policies behind. I can live anywhere in the world. I don't have to work either. But I live in Cleveland. And I work because I enjoy meeting people. All sorts of people. You, for example."

She put her hand on my crotch and said, "Let Deborah show you a thing or two about Cleveland—no strings attached."

She became a different woman. She seemed to shrink, even her voice lost a certain power. We wound up on the crushed velvet sofa. In the middle of the tight squeeze, my arm went crashing onto the coffee table and upset the crystal bowl filled with sucking candies. The bowl landed upside down on the floor, two of the brown candies staring up at me like my wife's eyes—"Your eyes!"— and I thought my rush of guilt would defuse whatever part of the brain it was that empowered my penis. But Deborah had an answer for everything. She pumped me up with her own sudden deflation. Her hands batted against my chest and back like the hands of an infant. She kept whispering things like "You're so strong," "You're so big," "You're making me weak." She whimpered and looked surprised and trembled like a virgin. And yet somehow her baby-weak arms and hands were responsible for every move the two of us made. Somehow they manipulated us, placing me first here and then there, and herself in one helpless position and then in another. Every so often I opened my eyes, thinking I'd catch her in her other form—the form of a large, strong, aggressive, directorial Amazon—but when I did, I'd find her shrinking and quaking and feebly trying to hold back wooziness and, when that failed, trying to cling to the ridge above utter loss of consciousness.

"How do you like Cleveland now?" she said when we were both finished, her before me, the original deep power again in her voice.

She stood up, put on her clothes, even blindly retied her perfect Windsor, all the while ticking off a list of rules and conditions and promises in the same colorless tone she had used earlier in going over the qualifications of the boys she had enlisted for my groups.

"I like to ski. I'm available for weekend ski trips given two weeks' notice. I also like the sun. I'm available for a jaunt in the Caribbean, in the winter preferably, given the same two weeks' notice. I will also meet you anywhere for any length of time up to a week within a one-hundred-mile radius of Cleveland given one day's notice and barring any unpostponable obligation I might have. If I have to get back in a hurry, I like to know I'm only a day's drive from home. I'll also pay my own way with regard to travel, restaurants, and hotel or motel accommodations. I expect no gifts, no tokens of your affection, no birthday cards or valentines, and no anniversary bottle of champagne next year on this day. In return, I will make no demands on you. No one will ever know that we are seeing each other. Our affair will be completely anonymous. I will never call you in the middle of the night to complain of loneliness or jealousy. I will write no poisonous letters to your wife."

But I doubted now that I had been able to conceal Deborah from my wife. Though my wife had never said a word, had never indicated the slightest suspicion, I always felt that I wore my guilt like ice cream smeared all over my mouth, that also being the effect Deborah had had on me; she was, when she loosened her tie, several scoops of vanilla promising to be cold and hard and then turning warm and soft as she melted into the crushed velvet.

I did not know why I kept seeing her, but it had continued for four years, during which time my company opened a branch in Cleveland, a branch I spent many two- and three-day visits helping to organize. I never took her up on her suggestion of a ski weekend or a Caribbean fling, but once I . . . I suppose I have to say I *reserved* her . . . for five days when I was in Cleveland that long on otherwise legitimate business. I was able to live with it because I never really thought of it as an affair. I only felt guilty when Deborah and I were not making love. Never during.

After my initial shock—of both her businesslike seduction and my uncontested fall—I found myself thinking about Deborah more and more. At first I only thought about her the way you think about a secret. She was good for an internal, unsharable laugh. But gradually my feelings became externalized. I'd pass a mirror or a shop window and pause to look at myself, stopping just short of flashing a wink at the lucky, but deserving, son-of-a-gun who gawked back at me. I began mentioning Deborah's name, in a purely professional context, to the people I worked with and to other men in the business whom I saw on occasion, scrutinizing their expressions for a telltale slip of unprofessional recognition when I dropped her name. Maybe it was because she had included a ban on gifts and tokens of affection in her preamble to our "affair" —reverse psychology—but I began to feel the frequent urge to send her sweet nothings, and then sweet somethings, and then, two months after meeting her, I was passionately and paranoically in love with Deborah Satin. The first sure sign was the fury I felt when Dennis O'Connell, a fellow moderator at a competitive company, lifted his vodka martini at lunch and said, "To Deborah Satin, there's absolutely no one like her." Had the very married Dennis O'Connell merely, innocently, known Deborah Satin in the dark of her viewing room, or had he seen her in the pellucid Caribbean light as well? I had to ask him indirectly.

"She looks like a concert pianist," I said, though Deborah had not so much as dusted the keys of her baby grand during the many nights I'd spent at her house. But Dennis would know what I was getting at. He shrugged off my allusion and said, "I see her more as an opera singer, a baritone," and quickly I searched my memory of her house and person and her every comment to see if O'Connell was doing to me what I was doing to him. Although I had come up with nothing evidential, I was sure O'Connell would one day call our Deborah a minute before I could get through to her and pre-empt my night of anonymous love in anonymous Cleveland. Before long, I viewed everyone who looked like he could have slipped through Deborah's personal screen as a threat and a challenge and a scoundrel, always imputing meaner and guiltier intentions to my rivals than to myself. I felt that if Deborah knew me better, she would give up her other men. When I saw her, I'd talk endlessly about my past, my present (except for my home life), my dreams for the future. And when that didn't ease my paranoia, I started talking about my wife, how wrong she had been to marry me, how unhappy she was now, how much more suited to one another Deborah and I were. Of course I told myself that it was just a ploy, a cheap lie, that I'd never leave my wife for a woman as independent and as undependable as Deborah Satin. But as long as the two of us were involved, I might just as well tip the illicit relationship to my advantage. During Christmas, I had literally ached for Deborah. She had let it slip that she would be in St. Thomas for the holidays, and I walked the crowded streets of New York as alone as an orphan. On Christmas Eve I stormed into Hallmark's and bought a dozen greeting cards. I addressed them all to Deborah Satin, signing each beneath a different closing: I love you; I miss you; You are beautiful; I had my Christmas the day I met you; Marry me; I hate Christmas without you. Then I went home and bled my deadly guilt.

"Let's have a baby," I had said to my wife. "Tonight. Right now."

I wiped the ice cream off my face and tried to squeeze my entire body into my wife.

The doorbell rang.

I pushed the covers away from my face.

"Go away," I whispered.

Again the doorbell rang.

"Go away," I whispered.

I held my breath. The ringing stopped. I waited for a door to slam, a car to start. But I only heard the ringing stop. I sat up, holding back the pain in my head and back and toe the same way I held back my breath.

My wife's one open eye stared at me. I thought I heard a tapping at the bedroom window, but when I turned to look, no one was there. Where was the cat? Hadn't she heard it? She always pounced on the littlest noise.

I thought I heard a scratching at the dining room windows. I stared through the walls of the bedroom and the hallway at the Andersen windows, my ears cocked like a cat's. If someone climbed the cellar door, he could look right in through the dining room windows. He could easily reach past the frame and make a scratching noise against the screen.

I sat for several minutes, waiting for the noise to reoccur, forgetting the noise only when the pain I was holding back broke through again and began to pound and grind and oscillate more intensely than before. I was done remembering. The last eight years of our lives did not seem to have any chronological existence. From our first visit to my wife's first obstetrician right up to the next pain-racked breath I braced myself to draw, everything existed simultaneously.

"I still say he's walleyed. He could fuck up the baby," my voice spoke as I pictured the overly jolly obstetrician facing my wife but looking at me. I was not certain, but I believed my lips had not moved. I could not be sure, but the words seemed to have come from me without my having spoken them.

"Know why I became an obstetrician?"

The voice was not a memory. I heard it. Live.

"All through medical school, every time I examined someone or learned about a particular sickness, I always went home that night and found the same symptoms in myself. I was a hopeless hypochondriac."

It was not my voice. It was older and jollier and automatic-sounding, as though the same words had been spoken a hundred times before to a succession of anxious couples sitting opposite the walleyed doctor.

"So when it came time to choose what kind of doctor to be, I picked obstetrics. That way I could never have my patients' symptoms, ha ha ha ha ha."

"I don't like him," the voice said. My voice. But again my lips had not moved. I even touched them to make sure. They were still, grimacing, trying to withstand the pain over my eye and in my temple.

"He turns to you and stares at me. How will he be able to deliver a baby? Watch him when he starts to pull the baby out. If he's not facing away from you, say something. Make him turn his head away so he can see what he's doing. He's liable to poke his fat finger through the baby's soft spot."

Then my wife's voice spoke. It sounded so much like my wife's voice that I snapped my head around to look at her face. She was still dead. Her small face had not moved, her lips were not moving, her one open eye stared blankly past me, my back ached.

"I'm happy about this," my wife's voice said. "You don't know how really happy I am about this."

"I love you," my voice said.

"But I'm afraid you won't love me when I'm fat."

"Of course I'll love you."

"I'll be ugly. I'll have to wear a sack; I'm not going to spend a fortune on maternity clothes. What if I don't get my shape back—not that it's worth getting back—but what if I wind up with a big floppy belly and ugly stretch lines and varicose veins and my teeth fall out because the little bugger uses up all my calcium? Did I ever tell you what happened to my mother when she was pregnant? Her hair started to fall out. She'd comb her hair and bunches came right out in the comb. She thought she'd go completely bald. She stopped washing her hair. She stopped combing her hair. My father said she looked like a madwoman when they rolled her into the delivery room—her dirty, snarly hair shooting out in every direction as though she'd been pulling at it for a year. I don't want to be ugly. All I've got are my looks. And my jokes. And if I wasn't pretty, I don't think I'd be half as funny. If a man looks funny, it helps his jokes. But if a woman's funny-looking, it's sad, isn't it?"

"You're pretty, Mommy," my son's voice said. "Especially your long hair and pretty dress."

"Don't worry," my mother's voice said, "you're thin, you won't put on that much."

"Oh my God!" the voice of my wife's mother shrieked through

my unmoving lips. "When? Who's the doctor. When are you due? Tell me everything."

"You're as thin as you were before," my voice said. "You're as beautiful as that day you posed on the wreck of a ship in your white outfit, the first day of our honeymoon, at the bar, the wrecked prow of a ship was the bar, and you sat on it in your white outfit and looked like the queen of all civilization."

All the voices came out of me. I could feel the vibrations of the vocal chords resonate in my chest. The ess of pain coiled a bit tighter, as though a masked torturer had turned one more tooth on the cranking gear.

"I'm glad that you and your mother are becoming so close," my voice said, as I snapped the brass locks of my overnighter and left for Cleveland.

"My mother is coming for dinner tonight," my wife's voice said.

"Is your mother there," my telephone voice asked, "because if she's coming over again, I'd just as soon let you two gab while I stay here and finish up a little work I'm in the middle of."

"Pretend I'm not here. Go ahead. Do whatever you want," my mother-in-law's voice half apologized, trying to defend still another visit but without letting go of a certain self-righteousness because she knew, she understood, she was proud of the strengthening bond between mother and daughter. At last they trod a common ground, although they did not exactly tread, they sat and knitted and reminisced and read Spock and allowed their imaginations to describe the messianic adulthood of the two- and then three- and then four-, five-, six-, seven-, eight- and then nine-month-old foetus. The unknowable female infant grew up to be beautiful and graceful, able to sing like a thrush, dance like a prima ballerina, a woman with a fine eye and a quick wit and a ravenous capacity for life. The unknowable male infant grew up to be any one of a dozen incredible saviors: a world leader; an indefatigable general; a movie star; a surgeon; a Nobel Prize winner in biology, having discovered, along the projected line of his celebrated life, a cure for my mother-in-law's diseased heart, while still finding the time to make my wife a grandmother and my reprieved mother-in-law a great-grandmother.

"Buh-buh!" the voice of the Nobelist said. Through me.

"Did you look to see if the fucking doctor's head was turned away? Did you?" my voice demanded.

"Where were you? Just where the fuck were *you?*" my wife's voice sobbed.

"I was with Deborah!" my voice shouted, and I could not stop it. The words passed through my closed lips like smoke through some impossibly porous screen.

"I know," she said.

I had drunk so much the night before, or this morning, I had forgotten precisely when, that now the sweet sour mash of bourbon in my gut was churning. A zebra—that is how it looked and felt—a fat-bellied zebra of nausea was crawling out of my stomach up into my chest and neck. I could feel it squeezing its huge haunches into my throat, its hot snorting muzzle inching up over my tongue. I gagged. I felt my heart stop cold. The zebra, its stripes winding like a barber's pole, exploded out of my mouth onto the covers, the sheet, onto my shirt—the shirt Deborah and I had bought for me— onto my wife's legs and chest and half-asleep face. The vomiting was not cathartic. There was more poison inside of me. The dusty tail or a manure-caked hoof of the zebra remained.

My arms began to move by themselves. My hands brushed away the zebra, pulled away the covers, began to remove my wife's pants and blouse. I watched as though it were a home movie; I knew so well the material of her pants, the buttons of her blouse, the yellow nicotine stains between my fingers, but I could not feel what I saw happening. It must have happened at some other time. But I could not remember ourselves posing and acting like this in front of the noisy, blinding Kodak movie camera my wife's mother had given us to record every movement of our son's life that his grandmother did not or could not witness in the flesh.

"I don't know why I had anything to do with Deborah," my unwanted voice insisted on saying. "But I paid for it. When we actually took off our clothes and made love, I hated it. I wanted you. And when I wasn't with Deborah, when I was a thousand miles away, she was all I ever thought about. At the moments of actual seduction, when Deborah would put her exotic hand against my crotch and gently squeeze and firmly lead me by my private parts over to her crushed velvet couch, I never resisted. What for? That's when it meant nothing to me. But when Deborah was in Cleveland and I was here, when she was grabbing someone else and leading him to crushed velvet, I ached and ached for her. It was impossible to resist my desire. Do you see? I ached for something I did not even want when finally I had it in my arms. And yet I kept going back again and again and again. I haven't seen her, not even professionally, for four years. I stopped when you went into the hospital for your second delivery. I couldn't bear the thought of another nightmare. I had to be with you. But I could go back tomorrow."

My wife's jeans were off now. Her thin legs, unsoiled by my zebra, flowed bonily into a symphysis of pale blue underpants.

"It was not so different with us," my wife's voice said in a tone intended to comfort me. "You had the desire to be desired. That is what made you ache for Deborah and stay with me. I did not say anything to you, because I was afraid of losing you. I had to make your desires my desires. If you doubted my devotion to you for even one second, you would have left—like Mickey, remember Mickey? My hold on you was how sure you were that I loved you. That I loved you no matter what."

The complicated nature of love, all kinds of love, seemed inscrutable, unknowable, as I slid my wife's blouse out from under the dead weight of her slight upper torso. The sight of her breasts was as surprising as my first glimpse of them had been years and years ago in our teenage heat on her sticky roof. But I was careful not to touch her breasts.

The sadness and confusion were more painful than my toe and back and eye and temple. In a delirium comparable to the wearing off of a lifetime of anaesthesia, I reeled and ached and held onto my wife's dresser for support. I held onto a kind of hard, external proof that I was still alive. I searched the top drawer for my wife's neat stack of underpants. A dozen pair, each one folded precisely in half, comprised two rainbow-colored piles. Then I slid the blue underpants off her. A piece of lint was caught by her spidery pubic hairs, and I picked it off and flicked it into the abyss, the black void which engulfed the immediate arena of my attention. If I looked away from my wife, she disappeared into the abyss. If I looked back at her, she appeared. I replaced my wife's blue underpants with the blazing yellow ones I had chosen from the rainbow.

"Thank you," my wife's voice said, in such a peaceful grateful, sympathetic tone that for the first time I wished in words that she were not dead. I shone my eyes into her face and said, "I wish you were alive. How I wish you were alive." But the voice sounded at once like other voices: her mother's, my sons', mine; it depended on whose voice I listened for. All of us had a reason to want her death to be a joke, one of her long, patient, self-deprecating routines.

I found my way back to her dresser like a miner groping through the dangerous curves of a cave by the cone of light emanating from his helmeted forehead. I searched the drawers for real counterparts to the certain outfit I pictured: stockings, a silk blouse, a golden necklace, for her hair a linen flower I had bought for her on our honeymoon. I found them all in different drawers, rediscovering her two crumpled brown bags in that same drawer with the linen flower. Perhaps the magically scented beige dogwood had fallen out of one of the bags.

"Go ahead," my wife's voice said. "Look inside."

Without a moment's doubt or fear, I took one bag out of the drawer and allowed myself to fall backwards, from a crouching position, onto the floor. I maneuvered my body into a curl that flowed with the pain, and then I tore open the bag.

"This is all that is left of her," my wife's voice sighed. "I had my pick of everything, but I chose only the things you see."

I saw a few faded pictures, several inexpensive pieces of jewelry, a small, green purse-size photo album, a crumbling certificate of birth, a homemade Mother's Day card, and an envelope addressed to my wife's first name. My wife had screened her mother's belongings, chosen only the most precious, desirable, evocative tokens. One by one, I examined the sad keepsakes. They seemed like relics from another age. Some of the jewelry was recognizable. I could picture the tarnished, low-grade-gold charm bracelet dangling from my mother-in-law's thin wrist, my older boy tirelessly fondling it and asking about each charm, his grandmother just as tirelessly explaining the significance of the miniature calendar, the miniature baby shoe, the miniature house, the miniature wedding bell, the miniature letter A. I realized for the first time that her beloved charm bracelet commemorated the significant events not of her own life, but of the life of her daughter. A speck of a red stone—not a real ruby—marked the date on the miniature calendar of my wife's birth; it had been the first charm to dangle from the bracelet literally a lifetime ago. The shoe signified my wife's first step. The wedding bell signified my wife's second step. The A was for my first son's first initial. The house was our house, the house that served now as the mockery of a mausoleum. There were in the contents of the bag assorted pins, rings, and earrings which I remembered her mother wearing, though she wore less and less jewelry the more her heart condition deteriorated, almost as if she were preparing herself for the nakedness of death. The loose, faded photographs, most of them resembling antique daguerreotypes, captured people whose identities were nearly faded too.

"That one is my mother's mother. That one is my mother when she was just two or three years old. That one is my mother's wedding picture," my wife's voice reminisced. "That is a card I made for her for Mother's Day when I was a little girl. She saved it all her life. And the envelope contains a few last-minute thoughts my mother wrote down while she was trying to recover from her operation. Most of the letter is incoherent and sentimental. She had no advice she wanted to give. She just tried to write 'I love you' in as many different ways as she could think of."

I wanted to do the same thing. I was jealous that I had not composed such a tribute. Jealous that my wife's mother had done it first. Angry that my wife's suicide had deprived me of the chance forever.

The birth certificate testified in no uncertain terms that my wife's mother had walked and breathed and laughed and cried on the planet Earth. The cheap green photo album filled with shots of only my children certified that she had lived her remaining years in their service and had tried somehow to fuse her imminent end to their new beginnings. Here and there a parental or grandparental head or hug had intruded into the snapshots of my sons. But my mother-in-law had scissored them out, even if it had meant leaving a strange hole in the picture, or an incongruous pair of arms encircling one boy's waist, or bits of adult fingers inseparable from one boy's tiny grasp. As jarring as her cropping was, one indisputable fact remained: there was nothing in any of the pictures that might distract from her focusing only on her grandchildren.

"She understood," my wife's voice mourned. "She understood

that the children were my aching desire and, like you, when finally I had them, I really did not want them. But my mother made the existence of a child bearable for me. She was more of a mother than I was. She tried to set an example. That's why I could not take your side when you complained that she was always visiting, that she was smothering the boy, not mothering him. You and I really did not want a child. You and I only wanted objective proof that we were happy."

It struck me now that my wife's difficult labor was somehow connected to the choking nausea she had experienced while she had tried to master smoking. Both were warnings: don't do it. What you're about to do will be fatal. But we did it because there was nothing else to do. I had to rid myself of Deborah. My wife had to satisfy her husband's desire to be desired.

I stood up and fastened the charm bracelet around my wife's thin wrist, and then I sat beside her on the bed and buried my head in the crook of her arm. I could feel my lips move against the cool skin of her arm as I spoke.

"I want you to know that I understand. I want you to know that I understand how suffocating your life became. I know that you could never look through our lovely house and see anything but jobs that had to be done—walls that needed painting, food that needed cooking, dishes that needed washing, clothes you had to iron, furniture you had to polish, toys you had to pick up. And a child you had to love. I know that that love was a chore for you. I know he made it an impossible chore. He gave you no reward. He only reminded you of your own frustrated existence. I know you smoked pot to make the chores easier, fun, unimportant in the silly, floating scheme of things. I know you watched television for the same reason. I know I stayed away. I cut myself out like your mother cut out the pictures of whoever intruded into her grandchildren's lives. I know when she died, your breath stopped. I know now that she loved you and the kids—no matter what. That she made you feel the way you made me feel."

But what I did not know, could never know, was the precise form and feel of dread that slowly had filled my wife. The mere observation of her life at home with two children she had not really wanted only described to me the causes, sometimes the results, but never the true, deep effect. How did she react to our first son's physical and psychological problems? Perhaps self-loathing, guilt, failure, cursedness—but I could not really know for sure.

And what about the relentless invasion of her privacy—by me, by the children, by the mailman and the repairmen and the supermarket clerks and by countless psychologists, psychiatrists, neurologists, optometrists, dentists, gynecologists, pediatricians. When our high hopes were pinned on a year or two of weekly therapy for the older boy, she had come to see life in terms of session fees. Denying herself a sorely needed winter coat, she had explained that a new coat was three or four sessions. A steak dinner was ten minutes of a session. Her perspective of life bent first through the abnormal prism of her own creation, which she was determined to fix. But she resented having to fix it. And having to fix dinner, too. And socks. And the younger boy's toys which the older boy destroyed. She had no time to fix her own hair or makeup or to update her wardrobe or to spend an undisturbed fifteen minutes soaking in a tub full of delicate, scented bubbles. She could not read a book or a magazine or a daily newspaper or her mail without a little voice pleading for her to play a game or give it something to eat. She could not settle into bed without first having to trudge up the stairs to close a light, open a window, retuck a cover, and, on her way back down the stairs, pick up still another toy or undershirt or sock or her own high-heeled shoes which either the younger boy had used as a boat or a bus for little plastic boys and girls and cows and robots, or the older boy had worn in his fantastic lust to be a girl. But it did not matter. My wife no longer wore her high-heeled shoes. She could not go out without thinking about the life that awaited her back home. So she stayed home all the time, where at least an occasional dream of a grand night on the town worked a small miracle. Better to desire than not to desire.

And then her mother's long, slow, painful death. The decision by her mother, supported by my wife, to try a risky operation. The depressing chain of symptoms leading up to that decision: shortness of breath, a swollen abdomen, weakness, the inability to roughhouse, even in her feminine way, with her grandchildren, dizzy spells which caused her to fall down and injure herself. She had broken a hip, and the bone's frailty had made a strong knit impossible. Every once in a while her left leg would give out on her and she'd grab at a table, a hedge, the shelves in the supermarket, the candy counter in a movie theatre to keep herself from toppling down like a baby learning to walk. Then, after the heart operation had been a success, the patient died. There was no one left on the planet Earth who loved my wife unreasonably so. No one left who accepted and loved her children—no matter what.

I know the result. The result is death. But I do not, cannot, know the effect life had on my wife.

"What did you feel?" I asked the cold, thin crook of my wife's arm. "Tell me your innermost feelings." But instead of an answer, there were only facts. In the end, that was all anyone would have to go on. The simple and also complicated facts of a spilled glass of iced coffee and a weaving trail of tiny shitballs. It was fitting that something as innocent and involuntary as the desire to drink and the release of bowels should have been the final cause.

I sat up. My pain was another stubborn fact. But its constancy diminished it. I could survive. Her white pleated skirt. Her white, flimsy high-heeled shoes. The rest of her outfit had to be found. The call had to be made. The second bag had to be opened. I pulled it out of the drawer and could not immediately guess the contents by feel or weight. Greedily I tore open the second bag. The tail of the zebra, the hard hoof, the gelatinous sadness which quivered inside of me as my aching body convulsed shot out with a scream. The cat flew into the room.

·

On a sunny Sunday afternoon, Ray Spaulding and his wife drove to the house of his wife's son by a previous marriage. Mrs. Spaulding had spoken to her son on the phone Friday evening and had sensed that something was wrong. She tried calling again on Saturday afternoon, but there had been no answer. She tried his office a few hours later, and there had been no answer there either.

Ray Spaulding parked the car in front of the house to appease his wife. "The big car isn't here," he said, "they're probably out for a drive or away for the weekend." But his wife wanted to make sure. She entered the breezeway off the back door and peeked inside. It was quiet. She rang the doorbell several times, but no one answered. Her suspicions were further aroused, however, by the failure of her daughter-in-law's cat to answer the door by scrambling up onto the nearby kitchen table to meow and meow.

Mrs. Spaulding walked out back and climbed the cellar storm door to peek in through the dining room windows. Again everything seemed to be in order. The Spauldings drove off, Mrs. Spaulding unwilling to be comforted by any logical explanation her second husband tried offering for the absence of her son and her son's family.

On the highway heading home, the unworried driver and his baffled wife passed a local police car. An hour later, the radio in that police car ordered Patrolmen Leonard Skye and Vincent Denby to the house which the Spauldings had just left. Inside the house, they found what promised to be front-page news in the local papers. The man who had telephoned the precinct was sitting on the floor, the receiver of the phone still in his hand. The man was naked and twisted out of shape, as if by a severe dislocation in his back. One eye, the right one, was shut tight. One foot, again the right one, was resting on a crumpled brown bag. Across from the naked man sat the fully dressed body of his dead wife, which had been propped up on a chair. The woman was smartly dressed in white high-heeled shoes, stockings, a pleated white skirt, a silk blouse, also white, a gold necklace, a gold charm bracelet, and there was an off-white flower in her hair. Her face was carefully, beautifully made up. Patrolman Denby called out to his partner from the bathroom. Skye found Denby leaning on the bathroom sink trying not to throw up. Behind him, in the tub, was the body of a young boy, eight or nine years old, his head crushed, evidence of recent water and suds glistening in the tub. A further search of the premises uncovered a third dead body, that of a younger boy—three, maybe four years old, Skye guessed—lying upstairs in his bed under a bizarre barrage of lights. Within fifteen minutes, three more patrol cars and two ambulances arrived at the house. By then the neighbors were milling about in full force. Patrolman Denby, who had a young son of his own, had to be restrained from attacking the naked man holding the phone. He said he didn't know what had come over him. Skye helped the naked man to his feet, draped a sheet around him, and escorted him to an awaiting patrol car.

The bodies were left in place until Coates of Forensic arrived to start his report. Only after Coates was satisfied were the bodies of the woman and her children removed from the house and driven to the morgue where Coates's brother, the county coroner, would finish Coates's report. At the station house the naked man calmly repeated the story he had phoned in to the desk captain. The naked man confessed to the murders of his wife and two sons. Four more times he would repeat his confession, his words hardly varying at all. But no one believed him. They thought he was crazy, but they did not think he was a murderer. And they did not blame him for being crazy. The coroner's office determined the exact times of death and a simple phone call to Harold Page Research, Inc., determined that it could not possibly have been the naked man—that is what the press dubbed him—who committed the murders. Moreover, no one believed that there had been three murders. The evidence—the fact that the naked man's wife showed no signs of having struggled—left little doubt that she had committed suicide. And that, in turn, left little doubt that it had been she, in fact, who had murdered the children. Everything fell into place except the naked man's steadfast confession. Even his own mother didn't believe him. To her dying day she would periodically shake her head, remembering that weekend she had sensed something was wrong, and she would marvel out loud that she had just spoken to her son that Friday night and she had just been there that Sunday afternoon peeking in the window—she had been right there! Nothing about the tragedy puzzled her so much as her own inability to have broken in somehow and put everything right.

Nothing at all puzzled the arresting officers, the Desk Captain, the chief of detectives, the coroner, the prosecutor's office or the dispassionate psychiatrist into whose custody the naked man was finally remanded. Only Coates, because his dreams were always filled with the inexplicable props which happened to be in the scenes of other people's crimes, only Coates wondered now and then about the strange contents of the wrinkled and torn brown bag. What importance, if any, had there been in that crazy bouquet of weeds and string and colored tissues and bald dandelions?